Grill Harmon

Heinz Grill

Harmony in Breathing

Deepening the path of Yoga practice

For seminars contact:
Meditationshaus "Wilhelmine"
Dorf 63
6323 Bad Häring
Austria

1st English edition 1996

Original German title:

Harmonie im Atmen,
Vertiefung des Yoga-Übungsweges

ISBN 3-98042-304-2

© Heinrich Hugendubel Verlag,
Munich, Germany, 1989
Copyright for the English edition by
Verlag für Schriften von Heinz Grill
Geert de Neve
Hohenburg 29
83564 Soyen
Germany

Cover Design: Ute Dissmann, Munich
Photos: Heinz Grill, Soyen
Printed in England by: Freedman Brothers (Printers) Ltd., London

For Yoga classes and events in
England contact:
Caroline Pick 0171 485 6902
(London) or
Karen Sussmann 01884 841832
(Somerset / Devon)

Contents

Preface

In the words of the book "Harmony in Breathing" lives a power which leads to meditation and a deeper tuning of the soul. The text conveys a feeling of inwardness and calm and contains a subtle energy, which opens the heart and gives a higher consciousness.

The thoughts of this book were born directly out of spiritual inspiration and therefore do not describe a doctrine or a world-philosophy, but are profound contents for meditation.

Heinz Grill neither had a teacher nor does his knowledge come from books. So in this book, it is not Hatha Yoga, as it has become known in the West, that is described, but rather two spiritual directions of Yoga; the Yoga of devotion (Bhakti Yoga) and the Yoga of knowledge (Jnana Yoga) join each other. This way of practice leads to a level of deeper perception.

He who is in the presence of Heinz Grill will sense that through him a power is active which changes the consciousness. Many people have experienced this in being with him and have thus learnt to practise Yoga in a new way.

The book does not describe a technique but conveys a deep spiritual message. This makes the contents initially difficult to understand. Many of Heinz Grill's students express this in the following words: "I find the book very pleasant to read but it is difficult to retain the contents."

We Westerners strive for a strong sense of personality and for great knowledge. Thus Yoga only makes sense in our culture if it can be lived and practised with devotion and the power of understanding. Technique alone is not enough to bring the soul into harmony and peace. Understanding and a sense of what the contents and the exercises mean and where they lead, must also be cultivated alongside the practical performance.

So Heinz Grill says: "Using exercises to reach a goal is pure selfishness, leads more and more into egoism and distances one from the actual soul reality. Cultivate devotion to the exercises combined with love of God, and an understanding of the laws and a new freedom will be granted to you."

Despite its deep soul-content the book is also suitable for beginners, as a comprehensive understanding is encouraged in a pictorial manner. The text is divided into individual, clear sections. It is recommended to read the thoughts repeatedly and to think them over. Paragraph by paragraph, the chapters lead ever more deeply into the reality of the soul. The chapters with the descriptions of the exercises are most suitable to start with, for example "The circle of the heart" or "Detachment and a new beginning". They are the easiest to understand. Only read a few pages at a time. Through reading you will take into your innermost the soul-warmth of the deep love which Heinz Grill radiates more and more.

Kirchreit. 27.11.1991.   *Rosa Michlbauer*

Meditative thoughts
for contemplation

For most people in our time it is very difficult to find a way into meditation, for the haste of the day and the powerful demands on the nervous system through present-day living and working conditions rob us of our entry within. More than before we are exposed to outer stimuli.

Meditation means deep pondering and calm resting with an image, idea or a concrete object. The thoughts are detached from everyday impressions. The consciousness becomes freer. New, unbiased experiencing is born out of the inner.

The following points are meant as an introduction to spiritual practice and ultimately also as a direct preparation for meditation. If they are repeatedly read, they open the individual to a new dimension of experience. An understanding of spirit and of the actual aim of meditation is stimulated. Thus an exercise can be started with more clarity and knowledge.

When the individual consciously sets out on spiritual paths, he is confronted with the difficulties of everyday life. The deeper the thinking touches inner regions and connections, the more the individual will recognise that forces are incessantly working in life, which cannot be considered as one's own driving forces, but whose origin is founded in the light of the cosmic.

Events and incidents from earlier phases of life sometimes become understandable only much later. Man lives in continuous growth. After physical development is completed, spiritual unfolding follows. This determines our entire existence. Our capacity to comprehend expands with increasing age and so earlier phases of life are better understood from a later point of view.

Life can only be understood if we become aware that we carry within us soul and spirit. These words are not simply to be taken as terms. We must look at them from an inner view. Looking and feeling into the connections of our being, gives certainty that our development continually progresses.

The spirit cannot be seen with physical eyes. Neither can it be comprehended through theorising, nor felt through a mood. The spirit creates life in us. We must become aware of what this means. The spirit creates us; it is the life that was given to us.

Life is a continuous exercise. It resembles a silent prayer. The spirit carries our entire existence; it creates the forms and measures of the outer. It is not matter which creates the spirit, but the spirit which creates matter.

A prayer is not bound to words. It is a silent listening into the depths of life. It leads to appreciation of the spirit. A prayer can be expressed in words or in silent thoughts; it can be seen in a gentle, aesthetic movement or in a silent touch of breathing. The appreciation of inner life which each individual carries in himself; of the life which in its forms reveals itself to the outside and of the life which is spirit, is expansion of the consciousness.

Our outer existence serves the inner unfolding. All everyday events help towards inner growth. The truth does not lie in the outer. It is neither a thing nor an idol. The incidents of life show the direction in which life should develop. The outer is only the servant. In all the exercises it is necessary to recognise this: inner and outer, subtle and gross, spirit and matter, heaven and earth. The outer is not the truth. If attention is directed to the inner unfolding, the spirit is found. The spirit is heaven within us.

Heaven is love within us. Love exists continuously. Inside we are connected with infinity. The inner life, which is love, is without beginning and without end. Let us become conscious of what it means to be infinite, to be eternal.

Spiritual exercise should lead to this consciousness. Within there are no boundaries and no separation from the whole. So the inner leads us to unity with ourselves and thus to unity with infinite life. The exercises of breath and the work with the body serve as a means to become conscious of the great power of the inner. From appreciation of inner life follows realisation.

In every individual, realisation of life proceeds. Silent, invisible powers work from within and create the outer conditions. Everybody is in a quite specific situation. Each present moment seems from superficial observation to be a product of outer circumstances. But these outer circumstances are determined from within. Love in the inner creates movement in the outer. We are guided by spiritual powers which are only given expression in outer form. All that happens we carry within us. Joy and sorrow, fortune and misfortune, honour and shame; all these pairs of opposites are but an expression of the inner working. Through them we are meant to grow. We carry the inner power within us. Through appreciation of the inner working we become one with ourselves and thus with our entire environment.

How often we worry about problems and difficulties. This is a state of disharmony. We want to change the outer situation as we are discontent with the events of existence. There is, however, no answer in the visible, and we cannot solve the problems of life if we only bring about a mere change of outer circumstances. We carry spirit within us. It is the driving force and this determines us. It alone is capable of dispersing the difficulties in outer existence. We must recognise that it is our own wish which determines the conditions of existence. We ourselves seek the resistances for through them we grow in life and mature into a higher consciousness.

Step by step we prepare ourselves for realisation, through the appreciation of love. Spiritual exercises are meditation, prayer, breath-training and also physical exercises. We use our body as a means to approach the truth in order to experience that inner power in silent appreciation.

It is important to pause once a day and to become conscious of the inner guidance of the spirit. Spirit is within us as love. Love is infinite. Every individual carries infinity in him.

In the outer there is no truth. Neither therefore is there a means which liberates us from the world. Silent appreciation in the depth of one's being opens the consciousness and the spiritual unfolding begins. This goes on in every individual. So we must recognise this power within us and learn to understand with this power. Through this we can recognise ourselves and also our fellow men. Love is at work throughout the whole world. Through love we are inwardly connected with all beings. There is no separation between us and the outer world. True self-discovery is not limited to seeking in one's own person, but requires deep empathy into the being of others. Everyone carries spirit within him. The great working of the inner is in the entire world. Spirit is in matter, spirit is in nature, spirit is in plants, spirit is in all lower and higher living beings.

Love in life is powerful. It is truth. Not any truth, but the truth. It lies beyond imagination. So we must overcome the outer senses and outer cognition through inner understanding. Beyond all tangible goals lies the inner mystery. This is the truth of life.

The more we want to achieve in an outer sense, the more hidden becomes the deeper meaning of life. The spirit is infinite. Let us become aware of the present moment. Only in the here and now can we behold the great power. The spirit carries our existence. The spirit gives us life. Let us become aware of this and live consciously in the present moment.

If we observe other people, then we must not judge their lives. What we do to others we do to ourselves, for within we are connected with each other through the spirit. No-one is released from this law of connection. If we judge another, then we condemn ourselves. If we say something bad, then through this we degrade ourselves. Many people are still asleep in a spiritual respect. They move very busily in material fields; they take no part in spiritual exercises. It does not matter. When we understand, we do not judge. All is a necessary growing. Spiritual powers are not visible on the surface. In the depth of one's being they work on inner growth. In silent work they create those powers which are necessary to ultimately gain spiritual knowledge at a later time.

The present situation offers the opportunity to realise the truth. Deep thinking out of the heart is necessary. Humility and gratitude are only possible in the present. For these are forms of consciousness, They can only be expressed in the present. The future is but a hope; the past is but a memory. In the present, the consciousness is free. So we can recognise life only in the present.

Nothing happens that is not carried through the power of love. Love is in us. Love is closer than anything else in the world. Humility and gratitude are expressed through love. Love is only possible in the present. Love can only

12

reveal itself in the here and now.

Only in our limited imagination is there separation. In truth, all is one. The spirit is unlimited. It exists in motionless unity. Outer life must become permeated by inner clarity.

Spirit is in matter. Spirit is in every atom. Spirit is in the minerals, plants and animals. However only in man can the spirit open itself to conscious experience. We must remain open to our environment. For in seclusion or solitude we do not find the right relation to the love of the inner. Outer life is necessary for our inner development. We must not isolate ourselves through spiritual exercises from our fellow men or from our environment. Solitude must only last for a short time, otherwise it becomes an insurmountable obstacle. In devotion and with gratitude for life, we will find meaning and our task.

Every spiritual exercise is like a prayer. It always expresses devotion and reverence. Love is the greatest. The individual "I" becomes one with love. This is not a state of emptiness. It is highest fulfilment. With love, the whole of life is experienced in deepest gratitude.

Thoughts contain great power. A thought is of spiritual nature. Now is the time when the great seed is sown through high thoughts. Thinking of the great spiritual law of life with appreciation and devotion for that which is alive, leads to inner growth. The thoughts which are thought now are the seeds which bring forth the fruit. In later years realisation will take place through this.

Within there is no injustice. Neither therefore can there be any injustice in the whole of life. The thoughts which each carries within himself move outer life. The higher the ideals, the greater becomes the potential for development in a spiritual respect. All spiritual exercise requires devotion and readiness for self-surrender.

Realisation is not a state of strain. However the paths require consistent striving and sound life conduct. Incessantly we must search for the truth and explore life from within.

Truth always expresses itself from within. It cannot be determined through the intellect. Many things in life seem difficult; problems give rise to doubts and cause vacillation. Through spiritual practice the inner task is sensed and becomes present for the consciousness. A power approaches and brings certainty. So the inner will overcome the outer. Life remains as the only reality; it remains within us. It is the lasting unity without beginning and without end.

Spiritual practice must first be learnt. It requires deep perceiving into the connections of life. Contemplation is the foundation. From contemplation follows appreciation and from appreciation follows understanding and realisation.

The breathing in relation to body, soul and spirit

In order to understand breathing in its living context, we must expand the purely body-related physiology through pictorial-spiritual consideration. Man is not only matter but is permeated by soul-spiritual powers in all his predispositions and character-traits. The body in its make-up, and the connected physiological processes are an expression of the great cosmic event. What happens within the material sheath is connected directly with a more highly ordered rhythm.

Man breathes from the beginning to the end of his life. Wherever he moves, wherever he goes and lives, he breathes. Conscious preoccupation with the physiology of breathing from an expanded perspective should strengthen the inner power of insight and contribute to a holistic understanding. This understanding helps man in answering the question of his existence and contributes to giving life a deeper content and meaning.

With inhalation one takes in the air in one's direct environment. With exhalation one gives the air out again. This process works in man continuously. Now a significant element of the soul is already given through this rhythmic process. With inhalation one does not take in only material air; one takes in, as it were, the sphere of one's environment. One connects more intensively with one's surroundings; breathes oneself into one's environment. Inhaling leads to coming closer; to deeper connection with the environment. Thus in an expanded perspective this can be called sympathy.

The opposite process is connected with exhalation. The air is given out. Now the respiratory muscles do not stretch and open as with the inhalation but contract, close in on themselves more tightly. The two lungs, which can be described as genuine wings, are, figuratively speaking, retracted. Thus exhalation corresponds to the antipathy of the soul. It signifies letting go, withdrawing, rejection. With the shrinking of the rib-cage man lets go of the outer and seeks distance. He withdraws from his environment, detaches himself from the sphere, just as with inhalation he actively connects himself with the sphere.

Sympathy and antipathy describe the two great fields of action of the soul. However these regions are usually unconscious to man. Also breathing is normally an unconscious, autonomous process. Breathing in and out comes and goes. One can say that breathing guides man; it leads him from without; it approaches him and penetrates him. His soul-state is determined through this. An individual breathing rhythm is shaped according to one's way of life and character-structure. A broad-ranging number of life-conditions is linked with it.

He who wants to understand breathing in its actual nature must visualise the greater sphere of activity. One lives continuously in the soul-process of breathing in and out. Usually one aspect dominates; sympathy or antipathy. There exists a relationship between ourselves and the environment. It lives in an invisible way in affection or rejection. We mutually exchange with our fellow men in a certain way. According to our state of mind, we live with respect to nature in a more active participation or a more passive passing-by. Sometimes we are more demanding, sometimes more observing towards the phenomena of life. Thoughts work continuously and express themselves in conscious thinking towards the outside. Thought itself belongs to the spiritual realm. The breath is directly connected with the state of mind and this state is turn in connected with the thinking. Thus the rhythm of the breath also forms the thought so that a certain way of thinking is revealed on the outside. Antipathy and sympathy are anchored in thinking as also in feeling. The individual in his being is connected as one with the coming and going of the breathing.

The physical breathing apparatus consists of the nasal passages, the nasal conchae, the sinuses, the pharynx, the larynx, the trachea, the two main bronchi, the lungs with bronchi and bronchioles and the alveoli. These alveoli are the actual functional units of the lungs. Here the oxygen exchange with the blood and the emission of carbon dioxide takes place.

Breathing is a movement and movement is expression of life. The diaphragm separates the chest from the abdomen. It is the most important respiratory muscle. The wave of the inhalation stretches the diaphragm downwards. The intercostal muscles of the rib-cage expand and give the lungs the necessary space to unfold. The wave of the breathing movement continues to the adjacent regions, the abdomen, the pelvic region, lumbar region, also to the shoulders and the neck. This movement is visible and also subjectively perceptible.

The respiratory muscles limit this movement, give it stability and closedness. It is, however, only a physical limitation. In the soul there are no limits. Just as the movement becomes visible at the chest and abdomen, so it leads further into the invisible world of the inner. The process remains beneath the perceptible threshold. However this wave takes hold of us in our entire being. Our body is penetrated at the level of the soul by the coming inhalation. Thus the breathing exceeds the boundary of our outer person and brings about a waft of inner liveliness.

With our senses we live in the outer, physical world. We perceive the images of nature and the daily events in their visible form. Yet in the depth of all appearance, a mysterious, invisible world is concealed. The breath is still perceptible at the nostrils, in the nasal cavities and in the upper windpipe. The movement of the respiratory muscles is also perceptible to the consciousness. Below the larynx, however, the wave of breath is lost in the unconscious. It is no longer accessible to direct perception.

In an exercise, however, we plunge with our attention deeply into our being. An exercise is always a process of becoming conscious. We do not only follow the outer movement of breathing, but also the inner one. The consciousness is directed from outside inwards. The power of the sphere working through the soul is significant for this. The consciousness steps deeply into that inner world of the unconscious. The breath is taken deeply inside and the wave takes hold of the entire person. Something alive awakens out of the depth of the being. Breathing is inner fulfilment. The consciousness of receiving and the sensitivity grow. If man becomes aware of the inner working, if he directs his attention from the perceptible to the no longer perceptible, then something alive flares up to the outside. This is gratitude and gratitude is a form of consciousness. The outer perception is penetrated with inner liveliness. He who perceives the inner fulfilment of breathing; he who plunges into the depth of his being, he will feel gratitude.

Steering the attention inwards is not related to a specific point. The wave of breath breaks through the perceptible, physical boundary. This sensitive perception expands the consciousness.

Physiology in its conventional sense speaks of inner and outer breathing. The outer breathing goes as far as the alveoli of the lungs; the inner breathing continues to the individual cells. Oxygen is bound to the red blood corpuscles in the alveolus, and with the arterial stream of blood is brought into the arteries and capillaries. There certain enzymes are active which finally carry the oxygen into the cells.

The more one listens to the breathing, the more one perceives in it the waft of the soul. Breathing cannot be understood as mere body-physiology. A soul-spiritual impulse is tied to the outer image. It is not we as human beings who determine the breathing, but it determines us. If we plunge ourselves with our consciousness beyond the outer boundary into the silent world of aliveness, then we experience gratitude. We perceive life; our cells breathe; they take the sphere into themselves; they are constantly in motion. Within us lives something greater. The cosmic realm is incorporated within us and the breathing shows the aliveness.

Particularly during an exercise we can perceive the quality of the breathing and sense the breath as a sensitive motion of the soul. With the inhalation the warmth of the inner increases. Oxygen meets the red blood corpuscles in the alveolus. Blood gives warmth. Wherever blood flows, there is also warmth . With inadequate circulation the limbs become cold. When the blood meets the breath, then the outer sphere connects with the inner warmth. The blood describes the individual "I"-activity. By saying "I", the individual raises himself, and the blood with its warmth is the physical carrier of this "I"-power. So this meeting of the blood with oxygen gives the power to act to the outside. When we give ourselves actively to the outside, then we can perceive this surging enthusiasm. With this a note of the soul is given inwards.

Inhalation gives enthusiasm and this is the sympathy of the soul. Exhalation brings detachment and that is the antipathy of the soul. Warmth is connected with inhalation, on the other hand cold is connected with exhalation. Carbon dioxide is released from the blood and excreted by way of the breath. Exhalation causes the enthusiasm to fade. The fire of the soul is extinguished. The nerves and the circulation are also brought to rest. The phase of exhalation is the time of physical rest. It is likewise important. New activity can only arise again after detachment. That which the individual perceives in this phase as cold is the calming of the body; the power to act disappears. Thus this phase particularly serves for becoming conscious and for contemplativeness.

Oxygen and carbon dioxide have very different effects on the body. Oxygen can be considered as the actual carrier and sustainer of life. Without oxygen man would fall into a state of unconsciousness after only a short time. All his vital-functions would ultimately also expire. So the most important significance is also attached to this element in healing therapies.

The exercises of breath training should contribute to better ventilation of the lungs and through the active training of the body they should expand the breathing capacity. With this an increase in well-being can also be achieved. With a good supply of oxygen the brain becomes clearer, the concentration better and the entire vitality increases. The student perceives an increase in self-confidence. The radiance of his person becomes stronger.

This is just one effect which is limited to the concretely comprehensible. It is, however, just one area of life. Oxygen affects the outer, visible life, and also takes first place in medicine. Its effects are known and can thus be used for the sustaining of life.

Carbon dioxide, on the other hand, is the end product of breathing. It must be brought back via the blood to the alveoli of the lungs, so that it can return to the outside via the respiratory tract. Otherwise carbon dioxide would develop a toxic effect in the body.

Now to understand the breathing in a soul-spiritual respect, the opposite effects of oxygen and carbon dioxide must be emphasized. The more actively one works, the more oxygen is needed. Much oxygen is also needed when the thoughts flow in a lively way. The brain in particular must be constantly supplied with this substance, otherwise fits of fainting would occur. Thinking continuously requires oxygen, because subtle oxidising processes take place in the brain. These need oxygen and with it enable thinking.

However, another aspect is also connected with life, which is likewise important. This is meditation and the inner experiencing connected with it. It represents the opposite of the outer, active aspect which requires oxygen.

The breathing changes in meditation, for during meditation the thinking becomes calm. The person meditating completely detaches himself from outer goals, looks inwards and opens up entirely into the consciousness of spacelessness and timelessness. He is physically as well as mentally completely relaxed as he does not identify with an outer impression or thought. The attention rests in the inner and the consciousness is free from the physical nature. Deep meditation leads one to a near standstill of breathing.

The person meditating does not now live on oxygen, but on the effect of carbon dioxide. During introspection he is, in his being, another. He does not take part in transitory happenings; he is not bound to earthly life. Nor therefore does he need any oxygen. The carbon dioxide does not now develop a toxic effect, but changes into carbon and this again gives the body enough power to be able to live.

The exercises of the breath all effect the consciousness. So there is also a change in the balance of carbon dioxide and oxygen. Particularly intensive in this respect are the Pranayama exercises of Yoga. Through training the rhythm of the breath one can achieve a requirement of only one breath per minute. But the exercises of the "Free-breath school" also affect the consciousness in such a way that the individual learns to live on carbon dioxide, even if only to a small extent. He builds up more inwardness and calm to his outward-directed consciousness. His being is prepared for meditative experiencing through the exercises. Thus he gains insight into deeper connections of life and finds a relation to God as the creator of the inner.

Free Breath Exercise

The name "free breath exercise" has been chosen because the breathing is allowed to flow uninhibited in its movement, in its natural depth and intensity as well as in its rhythm. Through movement exercises and certain meditative images, the breathing is trained in an indirect way. Through this it gains a soothing harmonising function for the body and also for the state of the soul.

Most people breathe incorrectly. With some people, this is clearly evident; with others it is only recognisable on a very subtle level. Correction cannot be achieved through direct guiding of the breath, for every physical appearance has a parallel with the state of the soul and with this, ultimately always a spiritual meaning. Intervention in the breathing rhythm occurs indirectly through physical exercise. So this chapter about free breath education should serve for becoming conscious of inner connections and furthermore should show various possibilities as to how one can use exercises for soul-spiritual development. Not only the physical body is addressed, but through deeper understanding and recognising, the subtle limbs of the being are at the same time also consciously perceived in the exercise. Through this the personality finds harmony and healing on a higher plane.

Free breath exercise is practised with various movements. Each movement affects the breathing and changes its depth, intensity, quality and also its rhythm. So for example, with slow movements, which are performed in a very conscious and concentrated manner, the breathing becomes softer, the rhythm usually slower and the depth of the breathing decreases.

With strenuous movements, the opposite is more the case. The breathing adapts itself to the changed conditions. It becomes naturally faster, deeper and fuller in its intensity. The freer the breathing is allowed to flow, the more naturally it adapts itself to the body's use of strength. The "inclined plane" is an example in which the strenuous movement requires more intensive breathing.

free breath as cosmic rhythm

inclined plane

These movements are also individually very meaningful. Here the effect of the exercise can often already be gleaned from the outer picture. If the student stretches the entire front of the body, for example as with the "inclined plane", then with this he opens himself with his being to the outside. The breathing becomes faster; above all the inhalation phase is very much emphasised. This means that with the opening to the outside he promotes the soul-quality of sympathy. Or else he extends his arms forwards, moves his attention out into the expansive space and with this tries to make himself more receptive to the environment. Sensitivity is expressed in this.

Free breath exercise is, in contrast to guiding the breath as is the case with Pranayama, completely safe. So the exercises are suitable for everyone alike, both for the spiritual aspirant as well as for him who seeks balance and harmony for the state of his soul. An inner experience is connected with all the exercises. With the wide reaching-out of the arms, the practitioner empathises with the sphere and experiences himself in this relationship from within outwards.

Above all, harmonisation and balance are gained through the exercises. He who practises them, rediscovers that calm and stillness in his person, which is otherwise overshadowed through restlessness of mind and haste of thoughts.

Although breath-work is in the first place work with the consciousness, all the exercises also have a very favourable effect in the most diverse problems. The harmonising of the mental constitution and the expansion of the consciousness brings relief or even healing for many illnesses and ailments. The inner organs which throw a particularly intensive radiating force on the body and through this in turn influence the entire state of mind and mood, are supplied, through the free movement of the breath, with healing energy. Through this intensive effect on the organs one perceives soothing currents and feels physically light and relaxed. The nervous system is strengthened so that receptivity increases and concentration improves.

Particularly the inner organs are connected with our consciousness. The state of perception during and after the exercise is very difficult to describe, for it is subject to direct experience. The more the organs are freed from congestion and the more they unfold their natural, undisturbed function, the more harmoniously do all the subtle energies glide and one feels more alert, more liberated; one feels as light as if one had no body weight. The consciousness in this state is opened and thus ready to receive new impressions.

Just as a pine forest adapts to the rhythmic movement of the wind, so the student adapts to the free flow of breathing. He perceives himself to be integrated with his body into a greater event and experiences breathing as a living, all-penetrating stream.

The breathing is a rhythmically moving wave. It comes and goes, takes hold of the individual, carries him, frees itself again and falls away outwards. In the exercise one consciously opens oneself to this gliding wave, observes the rising and falling. The will, however, does not interfere with this process. It remains passive like an observer. The consciousness is actively involved. The breathing is accepted; it is recognised as something higher. In a very sensitive way the student perceives his body. He experiences himself in his own form and devotes himself attentively to the wave of breathing. Thus he perceives himself in lively participation and experiences his surroundings with the movement of breathing.

The free breath exercise always takes place with physical movements. Similar to the asanas, the physical exercises of Yoga, either a certain posture is taken up or a flowing movement is performed.

What now does the movement of the body mean? Which inner aspect can be recognised in it? When the limbs are moved outwards, when the arms touch into the expansive space, we can feel that something meaningful is now happening in the soul. Beneath the physical threshold, a deep process takes place.

Our being consists of body, soul and spirit. Thus with every physical impulse, a soul and spiritual element is involved. Subtle sheaths surround our physical nature; our material body. We possess spiritual limbs in our being. So we must study breathing in a living context and pictorially expand our imagination beyond the purely physical. With the senses we cannot comprehend the inner event of breathing, but in the depth of the soul we can get a notion of its great meaning.

Movement is breathing. It is not to be understood directly like the physical breathing apparatus. But if we internalise the picture, then we clearly see a transformed breathing activity in the movement.

Just as inhalation corresponds to the body's fullness of strength and to the sympathy of the soul, it is now equally movement which, breathing into the expanse of the sphere, experiences itself. The return to the starting position corresponds to antipathy; to physical relaxation; to retreating from the sphere.

With movement it is not carbon dioxide that is released but lactic acid is produced. This shows the living, transforming process of the breathing in the movement. Both carry soul in themselves.

Now movement can be divided into two big groups. One is the dynamic physical movement; the other is the stationary movement, the static body posture. Once again we can look at these two different forms of body symbolism from an inner aspect. Here, coming from the physical aspect, we must direct our view towards deeper, inner connections. Through this we can get a notion of the hidden soul-element.

The dynamic movement which is now practised slowly and deliberately in the form of an exercise, corresponds to a human sense organ which has a very comprehensive meaning. When the movement glides outwards, the student touches outwards into the space. He prepares himself for perception of the outer. This corresponds to touching, to sensing through the organs of touch. The attention is pointedly directed to the subtler perception. At the same time, however, the student remains in the consciousness of his inner expansiveness and unlimitedness.

In this body symbolism we have that quality which corresponds to a human sense-organ. This sense-organ of touch is of an entirely spiritual nature, for it carries out an unbiased task of perception. It does not perceive only the physical, but also the spiritual. Born out of the super-sensory world, the organ of touch also retains its spiritual nature, but it is up to the receptiveness of our consciousness as to whether we actually notice the spiritual impulse through touching. It is not the senses themselves, but the consciousness which receives sensory and super-sensory things.

If the dynamic movement now passes into a static posture, we can, according to our train of thought, describe this as stationary breathing. The movement is submerged breathing. The physical breathing continues to flow, the limbs of the body, however, remain unmoved. Silence is experienced and it works deep into the inside. Silently the soul shows itself.

The body sensitises its organs of perception. While the student retains the static posture, he stays conscious of himself. He remains in alert circumspection and observes the subtle changes in his body and in his perception.

The experience is always on a physical and a soul-spiritual level simultaneously. Our body is differentiated into soul, body and spirit and is yet a uniform structure. In the static posture, the degree of becoming conscious is at its greatest. Via the senses, the spiritual is addressed. Those senses which perceive the world and which were born out of cosmic light, direct themselves attentively into the silent pause in movement. It is hearing. The individual experiences, in the static movement, that spiritual impulse of hearing.

With these images, breathing should be experienced in its greater field of action and the student can sense into a lively comprehending of his person. He can likewise develop more sensitivity towards others and through this stabilise his capacity on a higher level of consciousness. The forming powers of the soul-spiritual are perceived. It is not one's own impulses of the "I"-will which move the breathing. A great, all-encompassing event is connected with it. We breathe continually; we move and through our senses we continuously receive impressions. The experiences are varied and so, too the freedom of the consciousness is individually varied.

With our existence, a certain life-situation is given to us. One can say that it is imposed on us through the cosmic world-law. The individual nature of our person is not solely the product of our own wishes and wanting. It is formed through the co-operation of spiritual powers and one's own motivating powers. An inner structure has been given to us through our predispositions. Thus too, our body is formed, and to a great extent the state of our soul as well. We can express wishes, however we cannot freely unfold our will. Out of the present but not tangible, spiritual realm, we are determined in the depth of our being. Because the seed of the cosmic is contained in the inner, we carry eternity and with this our entire fate within us. All that we do, all actions and work, as all occurrences, are wanted from within, from ourselves. Nothing happens in our life which is not wanted from this source. However, this layer of our being remains superimposed by outer impressions and perceptions.

In the free breath exercise we experience a great shaped relation within us. Just as our person reveals itself in a unique way, different from others, we can recognise this individuality as the product of our own motivating powers and cosmic powers. These insights which are based on experiences of the consciousness, lead to identification with one's personal history. These insights also cause many contradictions in life to disappear. From the experiences follows acceptance, and in the development of the consciousness, this is the first step towards freedom.

During the free breath exercise, the rhythm of breathing in and out always remains natural. The rhythm is changed indirectly through body movements. In daily life this is constantly the case, for we move and the breathing automatically adapts to the conditions. The rhythm is influenced through tensing and relaxing. But thoughts also influence the breathing. Fearful thoughts speed it up; contemplative thoughts slow it down. Now in the exercise, this unconscious event is consciously experienced. In hearing, the static movement, one experiences the stillness of the inner space and letting oneself be carried by the wave of breathing in and out. In touching, the dynamic movement, one sharpens one's perception inwards and at the same time observes the gently changing vibration of the breath.

The breath exercise leads to more consciousness in the personal field and orders the inner conditions of body, soul and spirit. The relationship to the expanse of the cosmic can be experienced. The cosmic lives in the inner as in the outer. In hearing and touching the student experiences the relationship of his individuality to the universal.

Just as the expansive view of the open sea leads to an experience of unlimitedness, in the exercise it is the free flow of breathing which opens the consciousness for expansiveness and thus leads the individual possibilities beyond limits.

He who deals with life over a long period of time in a meditative way and perceives into the depths of his soul, will eventually gain from the experiences that knowledge of all embracing love. This experience does not show superficially, for with it a new reality opens up. It brings inner fulfilment; life quite suddenly is experienced without limitation through space and time in its actual magnitude. This is always a most drastic experience which cannot be described with words. However with this experience, every outer structure also breaks apart. This is experienced as intense pain, for the previously experienced reality is taken away from the individual; it suddenly becomes illusion. So pain is connected with this experience. The individual experiences the awakening of the spirit with the disappearing of the familiar reality. This step, however, requires prolonged preparation. In our existence we do not live the highest ideal; in our actions and work we do not embody selfless love. Yet it exists within us. We carry it as infinity within us. The exercise should lead us step by step closer to the appreciation of the universal law of life. The essential should be recognised and experienced in the whole of life. Spiritual development is becoming conscious of the love in the inner.

Through the conditions of our present time we live in a state of disharmony. Our idealistic imagination is separate from actual circumstances. This means that we want to, and also have to travel long paths of development. Unity in life is only possible through the development of the consciousness. Practising free breath should lead to more consciousness and should lift existence over the outer barriers. Thus on a higher plane the whole personality is stabilised.

Practical aspects of Free Breathing

The exercises of the free breath school have a harmonising effect on the body, an uplifting effect on the state of the soul and promote the consciousness and awareness. Through active physical education stability is developed in the spine, in the limbs and joints. This physical education is very important, for on it is built the basis for self-confidence.

If the body is stable and healthy, a good precondition for soul-spiritual development is given.

Take time for practising an exercise or an exercise cycle. If you have very little time, ten minutes is enough. However, these ten minutes should be totally at your disposal. While practising an exercise, step entirely out of daily life. The time which you take for practice should belong entirely to you. As long as you still have your thoughts half in your everyday-life, you cannot allow the breath its free movement. Therefore take this time for yourself and look inwards to the depth of your being.

Spread a plain blanket on the floor. The room for practice should be clean, pleasant and harmonious in atmosphere. Good outer conditions help you to distance yourself from the usual events of the day.

Light cotton clothing, which fits comfortably on the body, is recommended. If possible, light a candle before you begin practising an exercise. Practice is a time of contemplation. An outer order helps towards inwardness and allows practice to become a joy.

It is particularly inwardness that is significant. The exercises have an effect right from the beginning. The two essential basic powers of the soul are addressed through them: the thinking and the will. These powers have been given to man for his development, for life.

Thinking is bound to thought. If thought did not exist, man would not be able to make use of the power of thinking. Thought itself stems entirely from the spiritual realm. Just as a machine cannot originate without the idea of the technician, so thinking also requires the creative power of thought.

For breath-exercise this careful distinction is necessary for inner understanding, for it is particularly the thinking which is addressed through the breathing. If one immerses oneself in the streaming and flowing, in the coming and going of the wave of breath, then one detaches oneself from outer impressions and ideas. One listens to the breathing and with it listens to an infinite rhythm. The consciousness is directly addressed. This contemplative observation of the breath leads the thinking from outer goals to deeper knowledge. Things are no longer judged from outside, but observed through their inner nature. Thus through becoming conscious of the everlasting breath, one touches the inner side of life. With one's thinking one moves into a different dimension. One touches the creative, the thought itself.

Also one's will learns from the breath. This is likewise a deep process of cognition. How often does one get stuck on an idea or a matter? How often does one work desperately on a project and notice how it saps one's own strength? Man can choose in life, but he has no freedom in will. With his inner he is bound to a cosmic law. Often an outer goal takes the upper hand over the inner and one thinks that by achieving something one reaches a peak. A peak of what? If one becomes conscious of breathing and thus of life as the actual power, then one sees the transitoriness of one's actions. One becomes conscious of a much more meaningful value. The outer will to achieve loses in importance. One finds calm through knowledge of the intransitory.

The breath is the teacher for thinking and wanting. He who wants to find himself must become conscious of this relationship. The basic powers of the soul must mature in life. One cannot practise self-surrender and self-realisation if thinking and wanting are not trained. This is a natural maturation-process for the personality. Deeper experiences about life are gained through it. Breathing is connected with the expanse of the cosmic; it is the teacher for thinking and wanting. This is experienced in the exercise, for the exercise initiates a soul-spiritual development-process for life. The further task exists in consciously facing the events of existence. Thinking matures to clarity through active cognition, and the will becomes strong and persistent through humility in acting and appreciation of the cosmic law.

The exercises should always be seen as a separate event. They also develop more conscious breathing in daily life. One should not, however, attempt to constantly breathe consciously, for this would burden the nervous system and bind one's own "I" too much to the physical body.

It is valuable to perform one, two, three or more exercises daily. A strenuous cycle can be combined with a meditative movement exercise. If one steps daily out of everyday occurrences through an exercise of consciousness, an intensive working of powers unfolds which has a stabilising and harmonising effect on one's personal unfolding.

Conscious sensitising of movement (exercise)

Our present time is marked by sensitivity. The body is perceived in its subtle sheaths far more than in previous times. Thus the physical constitution has also changed. The nerves and senses in very many people are receptive to sensitive stimuli and impressions; the physical stability, however, is significantly weaker than before. This leads to more anxiety and unsteadiness in one's being.

Anxiety is a sign of lacking awareness. It means that the individual is not conscious of his inner and of his nature. The body possesses a soul, and this is overshadowed by outer stimuli. Anxiety makes life waver. It shows itself outwardly in various forms and to various degrees. So nervousness shows itself in states of increased tension or in exhaustion and inertia. Everyone probably knows the result of over-stimulation and its connected nervous strain.

It is essential to deal consciously with the various demands of life. One's own self must be strong. A power must exist in the personality, otherwise the individual becomes the plaything of outer stimuli.

An exercise is always a contemplation back to the core of one's own being. The "I" should be experienced. With this the essential should also be distinguished from the inessential. The ability to discriminate is necessary, particularly for the sensitive individual, for it gives him stability; it consolidates his personality. 'He who carries sensitive tendencies in himself, perceives and experiences the events of life more intensively; he takes in more and as a result also has more to process. He needs the active knowledge of discrimination. With this he maintains order in himself. The consciousness can freely unfold; it is not occupied by foreign impressions which are unwelcome.

Movement is a way of expression. From one's own "I", something is expressed outwards. With this the body is experienced; the breathing is experienced in its vibration. Through specific movements, the consciousness is addressed and thus one's own being is recognised in a certain way. The sensitive individual reacts perceptively, and thus each movement is also connected with an intensive experience.

The conscious exercise for sensitising the movement is suitable for everyone. It can be added to other exercises or else be practised as a single exercise. It has above all a harmonising character. Only a few minutes are necessary to do it, however these minutes should be used entirely for the exercise.

The movement is done in a standing position. The legs are closed; the arms relaxed next to the body. Gently straighten the spine up to the crown of the head and relax the shoulder girdle. Also relax the forehead and eyebrows.

Turn the backs of the hands to face forwards and consciously raise your arms. This movement should take place in such a relaxed way that you perceive the changes in space. Centimetre by centimetre, the arms rise up in front of you.

Also observe the change in your body. Pay attention to your shoulders being relaxed. The more the arms rise up, the more the chest and collarbone-breathing is promoted. If the muscles around the shoulder girdle become fixed, the breathing is hindered in its natural movement. Once you have reached the highest point with your arms, lower them equally consciously and slowly the same way to the starting position.

Remain with your attention in the weightless lightness. Shift your body weight onto your left leg. The eyes should always be slightly open. Your gaze however should not wander around the room. The direct environment is seen and sensed. Now gradually raise your right leg, straightened, off the floor. The movement is again conscious and very slow. Centimetre by centimetre, the leg is lifted higher until finally the tension in the thighs and hips becomes so great that a limit is set to the movement.

From the highest point gradually lower your leg again. The entire upper body should remain relaxed in this exercise. Always remain conscious of yourself and observe the subtle changes in the close sphere and in yourself.

Allow yourself time. Practise with each leg. Sense the coming and going of the breathing; also sense your body. Associate lightness with the movement. Consciousness means conscious abiding in the existence of life. In the movement an element of aliveness is revealed.

The exercise can be further developed in numerous variations. These can be formed according to your imagination. Raise, for example, one leg and both arms at the same time. However, always perform slow, conscious

movements, for it is particularly the slow raising and lowering which calls the consciousness into your being. Movement is conscious touching. A sense-perception is experienced right into the depth of one's own person.

A further variation, the practice of which requires a very careful distribution of tension, comes about if one guides one's foot up with one hand and straightens the leg in a stretch. For this maintain a calm stance; the shoulders are once again consciously relaxed. Only when the upper body remains relaxed can the stance be held without strain and wavering. Guide the leg upwards as far as possible. Then change to the other side.

Expansiveness of breathing – the triangle

If the breathing flows expansively and unimpeded, this means openness, trust and confidence in relation to life. If, on the other hand, the breathing is constricted, this indicates disharmony in one's being. A more or less conscious fear accompanies the soul. Fear is narrowness; the breathing flows in a narrow way. The consciousness is burdened by impressions and worries, and confidence in existence disappears. Just as the narrowness of a room has an oppressive and burdening effect on the mind, so constricted breathing has an inhibitory effect on one's self-confidence.

Expansiveness of the breathing, on the other hand, opens one's view and gives confidence in life. Trust grows and the opportunities offered by existence become attainable once again.

This short cycle consists of two exercises: A preparatory position which stabilises the body and an intensive stretching exercise. You require some ten to fifteen minutes to do them.

Begin in a standing position. The right foot is turned at right angles to the left. Place it stably on the floor and stiffen the knee joints. Leave your left arm relaxed by the side of the body. The movement of the dynamic phase should take place gently and in a controlled way, however not too slowly. Shift your weight onto the right leg and guide your right arm downwards until the hand touches the floor. The left leg is pushed upwards out of the hip. The shoulders should not tilt forwards. Twist out of the spine in such a way that the front side of the body remains open. This movement will present difficulties the first few times.

After about fifteen seconds return again from the posture and practise on the other side. A dynamic should always be maintained in the hip. Consciously push the leg outwards. Repeat the exercise twice more on each side.

This exercise strengthens the legs, the lower back and the trunk. In general it contributes to stability. As the body becomes more stable, the functioning of the organs also improves. The organs are connected with the nervous system; so the physical education also contributes to strengthening the nerves.

After completing this preparatory exercise, take the starting position for the triangle. Spread your legs about one metre apart. This leg position should describe an equilateral triangle. It forms the stable base. Straighten your spine up to the crown of your head and relax your shoulders. Observe the breathing and freely allow its rhythm and natural movement.

Lift the right arm vertically upwards, the palm of the hand faces towards the left. The left arm is taken horizontally outwards, the palm faces the floor. Take care in the movement that you always breathe sufficiently, as concentration on the body can make you forget the breath. The strong stretching out to the side necessarily requires lightness in the upper body. The eyes remain open during the dynamic movement.

Stretch in one plane to the left. Take care that the body does not bend forwards. Go to the point where the limit becomes clearly perceptible, the left hand gliding downwards along the leg. You should not, however, support yourself with this hand.

Persist for a few breaths in the greatest possible tension and then return again to the starting position. Also practise on the other side for the same length of time.

The image of this far reaching out to the side shows a high demand on life. The sides of the body are stretched and opened. The student gives himself unprotected to the exercise. Every step forwards requires courage and risk in life. With this direction of movement, the triangle symbolises the spiritual span of development of the individual. Reaching out far corresponds to the desire for progress, for learning, for growth and realisation.

Practise both sides twice more, persisting in the greatest possible tension and breathing quite consciously. After the exercise, maintain the stance with spread legs. The breath flows expansively and without resistance into the lung-cavity.

In a physical respect the triangle has an intensive effect on the region of the diaphragm. Particularly in this region there are frequently tensions or cramps. Breathing is hindered in its easy and natural movement and congestion and overloading arise in the inner organs. The nervous system and the circulation are also burdened by the constricted breathing. One's entire well-being suffers. Through the strong stretching in the triangle, this region is intensively worked through and the breathing begins to flow expansively. This has an intensively regenerating effect.

A supplementary variation may also be described: Maintain the stance with spread legs, and guide your arms straightened above your head. The palms of the hands are exactly aligned. Grow dynamically upwards, but take care that the body in its entirety remains light and that the stance rests in the triangle.

Detachment and a new beginning

This exercise is called Yoga Mudra. It is a symbolic gesture of bowing. In it one bows before a person, before a teacher, before nature, before the earth, before the universe or before that which is alive.

The image of bowing expresses deep appreciation and humility. He who bows with real devotion is ready to accept a new and greater task. In devoting himself to nature, man sees the uniqueness of creation. In bowing before the teacher, he acknowledges his wise guidance. In bowing before the universe, he perceives the infinity of the cosmos. In devoting himself to life, he recognises the life in the inner and in all beings of this earth.

Every insight is a new beginning in life. With it the old is no longer reality. One frees oneself from former ideas and life-contents in favour of new ideas. He who lives devotion from the heart is in harmony with the events of life. Through sincere devotion one receives the answers to the questions of life.

Everyone knows the decision of detachment and a new beginning. Often painful experiences are connected with letting go. One is not always ready with one's entire soul to forget a person or a matter. The new beginning is often attached to the past and brings further painful experiences.

This exercise should enable entry within and with the breathing should describe an experience of detachment and new beginning. The exercise can be performed in various sitting postures according to one's physical constitution.

Take the normal kneeling position, the cross-legged position, or if possible the lotus. Straighten the back and close the eyes. Become completely conscious of your person. Sense inwards, right into the invisible world of the soul. The breathing remains free in its rhythm.

Take your hands behind your back and interlock your fingers. The palms are then turned outwards. Continue to breathe naturally and bend the body forwards until the forehead touches the floor. With this the arms are guided, straightened over the head. They should be stretched upwards as far as is possible without force. In this way the shoulder girdle is thoroughly worked through.

Always continue to breathe consciously and persist in the tension. A natural deepening of the breathing occurs through the body-posture. After one to two minutes rise out of the position again and lower your arms. Observe the changes in your body.

This movement can be repeated several times as a preparation for the actual exercise of consciousness.

Remain in the sitting position and now change the hand posture. The right hand takes hold of the left wrist behind the back. Relax your abdomen so that the breathing can find its way into the depth without resistance.

In the subsequent bowing the breathing is combined with the movement. Breathe out slowly, lowering the body quite consciously forwards until the forehead touches the floor. The arms remain unchanged behind the back.

This movement should be performed with total devotion. Completely let go of your person while guiding the body downwards. A long pause in breathing is left at the end of the movement. In this pause, the forehead rests on the floor and the entire body is still. (picture p.45)

As soon as the urge to breathe in comes, slowly straighten up again with a big breath. While straightening up you can consciously fill the lungs from the bottom upwards.

Devote yourself to the breathing as a higher rhythm. The inhalation and the exhalation describe the great opposites of life. In between lies the pause in breathing. In this phase you should fully sense inwards into the depth of the soul. The body is like a flower; light, free, untouched by the polar opposites of thinking. The more you let go of your outer face the more audible becomes the stillness of the inner. The consciousness grows.

Perform the movement several times. Then let go of the hand position again and still remain upright in the sitting-posture. The breathing should flow without resistance into the depth. Tensions in the respiratory muscles are usually eliminated by this exercise. For their cause lies in holding on to certain thoughts or belief-patterns.

Yoga mudra is an exercise of consciousness. The new beginning awakens with the understanding that it is one's own inner attitude which leads to rigidity. One's own thinking blocks the free breath. In a simple way, free breathing can once again be experienced in the sitting posture. Bring the arms, straightened, upwards above the head and the palms of your hands together. Breathe freely and leave the shoulder area relaxed with the spine gently stretched.

The infinite circle of the heart

Everybody yearns for peace and security. One goes one's way in life as a seeker and proceeds through various stages of development. As a child one accepts the caring hand of parents; in one's youth one acts out one's yearning in passionate urges, and in adult years one finally seeks security in a relationship to a person or to one's children. However, yearning which can never be entirely fulfilled always remains. This yearning springs from an inner wish of the heart which carries within it a deep spiritual demand. The yearning persists until one's own wish has been transformed into a giving force. Desire is transformed into love for people.

This exercise is an inner experience. The heart is the organ which is opened for this circle described by the hands. Imagining the circle, which gives itself more into the expanse with every movement, bestows that giving force which exists in every individual. A circle gives security. It is closed, round; it is without corners. This gesture in particular expresses gentleness and well-being.

The movement opens the individual out of his narrow thinking and wanting. If the heart becomes taking, then it closes up, for it is a giving organ. It wants to show itself to the outside. It wants to allow participation; to be there for others. If the wish for affection is fixed on one's own interest, the other person is rejected. From the yearning for security, arises desire and the heart is no longer ready for love of others, but only for one's own possessive wanting. This is always a painful experience.

The image of the exercise describes the expansiveness which is connected with the heart. With every additional circle which the individual describes, he opens himself out of his limited attitude and takes part in the lively side of life. With the expansiveness of the heart, one's own yearning for appreciation is transformed into a giving force. The individual no longer sees his demand on life but puts the power of his heart into the circular movement as the possibility of experiencing unity and unlimitedness.

To practise, take a simple sitting posture. The cross-legged position, the lotus or the normal kneeling position are suitable. Put your right hand in

your left. The eyes should remain slightly open. Relax the muscles of your eyes and keep your gaze in the near distance.

Relax the shoulders, the neck, the rib-cage and the abdomen. The breath flows freely and is perceived in its movement. Let go of thoughts of wanting to achieve. Only in the here and now is creative activity possible.

Now guide your arms upwards so that the tips of your middle fingers touch slightly above your head. The palms of the hands face downwards.

The elbows are gently turned outwards so that a sensitive opening can be perceived in the arm position.

The circle of the heart is invisible. Do not try to see it. Only use your sense of touch. Let your hands glide apart and with this slow movement

describe the circle. Your breath continues to flow uninterrupted like the stream of a calm river. Enter into the imagination of the circle and let

yourself be guided entirely by your sense of touch.

When your hands have come down, the palms face upwards. Imagine holding this circle in your hands. This circle lives directly before you.

Now glide upwards again along the circle. Allow your hands to follow the natural impulse and thus to open further outward. The circle of the heart grows into the expansiveness. The sensing movement leads to the perception of calm and peace.

Security only exists through quiet appreciation of life. Whoever stands against life and disturbs the natural order, follows the path of separation. He demands instead of giving. The circle of the heart shows harmony and symbolises unity. This is the recognition of a greater power. One's own wish is transformed through a sensitive experience. The feeling unties its attachment to the body. The coarse becomes the subtle.

Describe the circle several times, guided by your perception. If it expands, then allow the expansiveness. The tactile sense of your hands and your imagination will guide you.

Finish the exercise by bringing your hands down again to the starting position. Put your right hand in the left and remain for a few more minutes in this calm position.

Expansiveness and unity

This short cycle of three exercises should lead you to a free, expansive flow of breath. There is a strong demand on the muscles of the abdomen and of the back. Through this the respiratory muscles are freed from tensions. At the same time the heart organ is penetrated by subtle energies. This leads to a deep perception of oneness. You need fifteen minutes to practise, including a short relaxation.

Begin in a standing position. The legs are spread almost a metre apart. Let your arms hang loosely next to the body, and with ease direct your gaze at the level of your heart. The breath should flow freely and should be felt deep inside. Wait in this simple standing posture until you can sense a feeling for the here and now.

Turn the palms of the hands forwards and guide your arms up sideways next to the body in a slow movement, remaining conscious of your inner. When the arms are the same distance apart as your legs, turn the palms backwards and come up onto your toes. The movement becomes a static posture. The position is called the St. Andrew's cross.

Always breathe consciously and sense inwards to your heart. The body as something external should for moments be completely forgotten. In the heart lies the consciousness of the spiritual "I". It is the seat of the conscious soul-power. Let this consciousness unfold out of the inner.

If the toe position becomes too strenuous, simply go down on your heels again. After one to three minutes, release the position by slowly guiding your arms downwards. Remain for a short time and then lie on your front on your mat.

The next position is a classical basic Yoga posture: the bow. Powerful effort is required to practise it. Take hold of your ankles and place your forehead on the floor. Relax your shoulders and become conscious of your spine.

The following movement must occur through the contraction of the back muscles. The legs must not be pulled up with the hands. The arms merely hold the bow in a closed form.

From the lower back, decisively push the thighs up. Also tense the middle of the spine and expand the rib-cage forwards. Breathe as much as the input of strength demands. Remain for as long as possible in the active stretch. The shoulders must not be fixed; neither should they be higher than the knees.

This position gives the breathing expansiveness. The more powerfully you go into the tension from the back muscles, the more intense becomes the whole energy flow and circulation. The inner organs are vitalised and thus strengthened in their function. If one pulls on the arms, then the spine is not stretched from the middle, but is fixed in the shoulder region. The expansive flow of breath with its regenerating effect does not take place.

Then take a sitting posture again. The legs are drawn up towards you, the feet placed on the floor. Raise your arms straightened above your head and place your palms together. Quite consciously straighten up the rib-cage, so that you get the sensation that the back is stretched between the shoulder-blades. From this position, the legs are raised so that you have to hold your balance (c.f. picture p.54).

Now in slow movements change the angle between back and legs. In doing this you can direct your attention to the raised rib-cage. The longer this posture is held, the more the body begins to tremble. Nevertheless, try to retain the strong tension and also to leave the breathing free.

If one keeps one's attention on the region of the heart in this position, one will experience a clear feeling of serenity during the great tension.

Then return to the relaxation position on your back. Let go of the body and its muscles. Impulses stream out of the heart. They give unity and peace to the expansiveness of breathing.

The plough

An exercise should again and again be a new experience for you, even if you have already often performed it. Approach the exercise openly and without expectation, for as soon as you pursue a specific goal, you distract your attention from the inner existence and with time tiredness will develop in practising. Every exercise is always in some way a new beginning in life; a re-ordering within the personality. The old is thus no longer valid.

The image of the exercise reminds one of the form of a primitive, old plough. Hence the name. The plough breaks up the soil so that the seeds find new, fertile ground. In the exercise, the individual contemplates deeply inwards, into the depths of his very foundation. He burrows into his inner world. So he finds within himself that answer for life which he receives through identification with the core of his being.

Lie on your back. The legs are closed; the palms of the hands rest next to the body on the floor. Breathe out consciously and at the same time raise your legs. Breathe in, guiding the legs over your head.

This movement should be consciously combined with the breathing, as through this the natural depth of breathing will be retained. Now in a slow, controlled movement, guide the legs further until the toes finally touch the floor. If this is not possible, then simply leave the legs in the air.

In the actual basic posture the legs are straightened completely, the arms are guided behind the back and the fingers interlocked. Continue to breathe quite consciously. Particularly in the plough the strong inner pressure can make you forget to breathe. The longer you remain in the pose, the more the rib-cage adapts to the unusual position, and the spine also becomes accustomed to the stretch; thus with increasing holding-time the position becomes easier.

Hold the position for at least two minutes. Then return to the relaxing position on your back, or perform the following variations:

Lower the knees to the left and right of the head and with your arms reach over the knee joints, so that you can take hold of your elbows with your hands. With your attention, enter entirely into the narrowness and closedness of the body.

In this variation, the cervical spine is strongly stretched. An experience of pressure can be felt. After some time open up again by taking hold of the feet with the hands and pulling the legs to spread them wide apart. Here you must take care that you do not sink backwards. Push yourself actively out of the back towards the legs.

Always breathe consciously and allow the free rhythm. Through the strong pressure of the rib-cage the breath is compelled to flow into the depth of the abdomen. Continue to retain the dynamic in the back and push yourself as far as possible towards the legs into the position.

The plough pose has a particularly intensive effect on the rib-cage and abdomen. The inner organs are thoroughly massaged through the strong inner pressure and thus strengthened in their function. Afterwards the breath flows effortlessly and deeply. The back is stretched in all parts. This leads to greater flexibility and strength.

In the plough, the stretching must not be forced. The spine should go into an even curve and thus into an evenly spread tension. This leads to the healing effect with a freeing sensation.

The more you move into a stretching exercise, the more you expand your potential. The limits in your personality are shifted. The spine is the central axis of the personality. Its flexibility shows the potential which can be reached in life. The more it can be stretched, the wider becomes your capacity. In a physical respect, strength signifies firmness and flexibility. In a soul-spiritual respect, it describes the ability to respond to the demands of everyday life with one's own activity.

If your back is already very flexible, then you can do a more demanding position. From the normal basic position, lower your knees behind the head onto the floor (c.f. picture). With this, the spine comes into an even, strong curve. The free breathing must be maintained despite the extensive stretch.

The plough pose can be combined with the shoulderstand (p. 86), as both exercises require the same starting position and are similar in their calm and yet inwardly dynamic character.

If you want to continue the exercise-cycle, the classical Yoga exercise "Matsyasana", the fish, is suitable after the plough and its variations. Lie on your back to practise and bring the hands underneath the buttocks. The legs are closed and remain relaxed throughout the entire exercise. Bring yourself up, on your elbows; tense the thoracic spine so that the rib-cage and head rise, and then with constant tension of the thoracic spine, place the head on its crown. Hold this counterpose to the shoulderstand and plough for a duration of two minutes.

Inner communication

Language is the most important medium of communication. It is a natural need of man to share with others, to speak with others and to communicate common events and experiences. Language is a mediator which man uses in order to gain understanding in being with others and to receive answers for existence.

Language is the outer medium of communication. The spirit carries inner communication. The spirit links people to each other. Spirit fills the entire universe; spirit is in every individual. In the spirit there is no separation. If one becomes aware of this, then one recognises that every thought that one sends out also concerns the being of the other. Whatever one does to oneself, one does to the other. That which takes place beneath the visible threshold is an inner communication. It is bound to a higher working.

The course of our life is subject to laws. The often hidden wish to live love, to realise love is common to everybody. Love is not a romantic state. It is a state of inner awareness, of gratitude through consciousness of life. There exists a connection between all people through this inner wish. As every individual desires love for himself and others, there exists a direct inner communication. However, this cannot be perceived like language because it is not audible; one can only become conscious of it.

This exercise is a meditative sensing inwards, into the inner connections. It contributes to harmonious exchange with the environment. Subtle energy currents penetrate one another in the heart. The more balanced their flow, the more peace and fulfilment is experienced. From this contented, spiritual attitude, the desire quite naturally arises to let others partake in one's own peace.

This consciousness exercise is very good to combine with other Yoga exercises. It is also suitable as the beginning of a meditation. Take a simple kneeling position. Place the right hand in the left and let the hands rest on the thighs. Relax the face, the eyes, the jaw and jaw muscles. Wait for a few minutes until your thoughts have calmed down to some degree. The exercise should be started with a peaceful attitude.

The breath remains untouched by your will. Observe its flow. The more composed your attitude becomes, the more steady and subtle the flow of breath becomes.

Leave the eyes gently closed or half open. Raise the arms to the level of the shoulders and bend the lower arms vertically upwards. The palms of the hands face forwards; the hands should not tip backwards. Breathe fully consciously, without however, guiding the breath in any direction. Become conscious of the soul-quality in your being. Through the calm, motionless posture, inhalation is internalised as if you were breathing in the scent of a flower and perceiving it within you.

Completely forget your body and the tension in the arms. The breathing carries a sensitive perception right into the centre of the heart. Remain in this position for about one to three minutes.

Then guide the hands forwards in a very slow movement, until the palms meet in front of your heart in the prayer position. This movement symbolises the uniting of polarities: masculine and feminine, positive and negative, activity and passivity, sun and moon, right and left, joy and sorrow, honour and shame. When the hands are brought together, this gesture suggests the uniting of life's pairs of opposites. The heart is the very place in which the dualities dissolve.

During the exercise become conscious once again of the infinity of the spirit. All beings are connected with each other through the spirit. That which you think is carried by the inner thought. That which you want is guided by the infinite will. Consciously let go once again, therefore, of your outer "I" so that a greater current can work through you. The heart becomes open with the knowledge of the love in the inner; the love which connects all beings with each other.

Very slowly and consciously, open the hands and turn the palms outwards. Remain conscious of your modest attitude. In humility, the higher steps from the light into one's own world.

Open yourself further and further outwards with this movement, completely letting go of your will. Only remain conscious of the heart.

The heart radiates love outwards. The more selflessly you open, the more power will flow through you with this movement. Inner communication is not subject to your will, but it is bound to a greater working.

The joy of the heart awakens from the consciousness of higher life. Just as communication on earth is accompanied by a much more subtle communication in the spiritual worlds, so visible, earthly life is accompanied by an eternal life in the spirit.

Life on earth is visible. Eternal life in the spiritual dimensions is invisible. Open your heart for these high thoughts and you will be filled with an inner, indescribable joy. This is the deep feeling of life's so hidden laws of truth.

Head-knee pose with side-twist

The head-knee pose – "Paschimothanasana" in Sanskrit – is one of the most important basic Yoga positions. The back of the entire body is stretched; above all the spine is stretched lengthways. This strong stretch unfolds an intensive activity of forces. One can also describe this Yoga posture as one of the most important exercises for the breathing.

The image of the exercise: As long as an individual faces the outer world, he holds his back upright and his head high. If he reflects inwards, then he lowers his forehead and closes his eyes. In the head-knee pose, he closes himself up completely; he also lowers his upper body. He senses into the very depth of his own foundation. Whatever happens around him does not interest him; he enters into his own world. He opens himself out of this world once again through the twist, but he keeps his eyes closed. He remains untouched by outer impressions. Only the breathing is received in expansive waves. The student remains in his bowed posture and experiences the breathing with devotion and gratitude.

This exercise is good as preparation for a meditation. One experiences the tensions in one's body; one consciously confronts the relationships within the body. The body reveals to the outside the inner side of one's being. Every tension has a meaning. The spine is the axis of the personality; with it the individual stands upright in life. In each individual it has developed differently in flexibility and stability. The directions of movement of the spine and their state of development point to the different fields of body, soul and spirit and their interconnections. For some people this position will be easy; for some it will pose great difficulties.

Take a little more time to practise this exercise. This movement should be developed without force. However you should put a certain decisiveness into it in order to overcome the existing resistances with time. In cases of serious spinal trouble or diseases of the vertebrae, one should work with particular care.

Begin in a sitting position with straight legs. Raise the arms above the head and stretch yourself up high starting from the lumbar region. The chest is also raised.

Turn your attention inwards so that during the exercise you perceive what is going on in your body and in your mental state. Maintain the lengthways stretching and bring the spine forwards. The starting point of the movement is in the lower back. You must determine the extent of the movement according to your flexibility. If possible, grasp the feet; if this is difficult, grasp the shins.

In this position there should be no crease in the abdomen, as this would hinder the diaphragmatic breathing. The strong inner pressure would also make the exercise a strain. First the abdomen touches the thighs; only then can the head be lowered onto the legs. Always remain in a dynamic of the lower spine. You can give some pull with your arms, but the shoulder girdle must not become fixed. When you have reached the limit of your tension let the body become calm and sense inwards.

Remain for at least two minutes in the static phase. There is no upper limit to the time period. The longer you remain in the position the more intensive becomes its effect. The nerves are strengthened; the digestive system is vitalised. All the inner organs are thoroughly worked through and thus decongested. Thus the head-knee pose gives a pleasant feeling of alertness and calm.

Rise out of this position after two, five or ten minutes and straighten the spine far upwards again. You can do the movement several times. The static phase should always be consciously experienced.

Out of closedness, the opening to the outside takes place. Straighten the spine far up again and then place your left hand on the right side of your waist. The palm faces outwards and the back of the hand lies against the body.

Pay attention to a free flow of breath. Twist the spine to the left, beginning from the pelvic region, and always maintaining the stretch along the length of the back. The start of the twisting movement in the pelvic region is very important, as through this the spine comes into an even twist.

Always keep your attention on the spine and stretch downwards towards the legs. This movement is not a bending, but an active stretching through the dynamic of the lower back. Go as far as possible into the position. The twist is maintained. With the right hand you can take hold of the feet or shins. (c.f. picture p.67)

Persist in this position as calmly as possible. The breathing becomes a little faster, but nevertheless a calm and peaceful feeling is experienced. Consciously keep the dynamic in the lower and middle back.

After one to two minutes, release the position and straighten up the spine again. Practise on the other side for the same amount of time.

After you have practised on both sides it is good to take the relaxing position on the back for a few minutes (exercise p.99).

The head-knee pose leads to a natural deepening of the breath. This contributes to a calming of the body and a stabilising of the nervous system. The twist to the side opens outwards. It brings about a sensitive perception. The energies flow more intensely upwards along the spine and lead to alertness and clarity in one's thinking. An inner note becomes perceptible in one's feeling.

The scales

The scales is an exercise which strengthens the body. It is suitable for everyone, despite the difficulty of the end position, as it need not be immediately performed with total perfection.

The position strengthens the muscles of the legs and trunk and gives the rib-cage more support and firmness. One's entire stability is improved and thus wide-spread symptoms of degeneration, which are a result of incorrect exertion, can be prevented. The upright sitting position is also easier with a stronger back.

The image of the exercise: The student begins from a stable posture and from this posture he allows the tension in his back to grow. He stretches his trunk as far as possible. Then he leaves his secure stance and moves into the daring horizontal position. He remains with only one leg on the ground. Just as in life, a step into the new is easier if there is stability and firmness, so the exercise only acquires form and character if there is stability of the body. Whilst standing on one leg, the student must maintain a high degree of tension, and at the same time must allow the wave of breath to flow freely.

To practise, take a standing position. The right leg is placed with the foot pointing straight forwards; the left leg is a little behind and the foot is turned outwards. The distance between the feet should be a maximum of thirty centimetres. Turn the whole upper body to face forwards and keep the head raised. Fold the hands together in front of the chest. The knee and hip joints of both legs should be kept rigid.

Direct your attention to the breathing. Take particular care that its movement is free. The concentration on the body should not lead to an interruption of the flow of breath.

Begin the dynamic phase slowly and consciously. Raise the folded hands higher and higher above your head. This movement is formed from the back. The spine grows into the tension. The chest is stretched upwards so that the spine is stretched throughout its upper half. The shoulder and neck region should remain as relaxed as possible.

The further you go into the tension, the faster the breathing becomes. Allow this consciously. Persist in the maximum stretch for a short time. Then shift your weight entirely onto your right leg. Bring the body into the horizontal position by tilting the trunk forwards and stretching the left leg outwards.

The breathing will become even faster and shorter with this movement. Maintain the tension out of the trunk in both directions. You should get the impression that your body is being pushed powerfully out of the centre into the horizontal plane.

Hold this position, if possible, for half to one minute. Then in a controlled way return to the standing position on both legs. The breathing becomes calmer again. Guide the hands back to the level of your rib-cage and stay standing consciously, remaining in the subsiding tension.

Only when the wave of the breath is allowed to move freely during the entire exercise, can the pleasant perception of flowing and warmth in the body arise with its connected regeneration. If, on the other hand, the breath is held as a result of the intense effort, congestion forms in the neck. The harmonious flow through the body is broken off.

Also practise on the other side, reversing the position of the legs. After practising it is good to close the legs and to let the body hang forwards in a relaxed way. Remain like this until a feeling of complete relaxation in the chest, shoulders, arms and neck has developed.

As soon as you have securely mastered the basic position of the scales, you can practise further variations. The first of these is the swallow. The expression of this position resembles that of a flying swallow. From the scales, guide your hands out to the sides and backwards. Remain for about half a minute in the free flow of the breath.

At first it will be difficult for you to hold your balance in the scales, and the movement is also very strenuous. After repeated practice, however, it will soon be possible to hold the end position in the free flow of the breath.

Persist in this standing position and bring the arms further back until the hands join behind the back. Also hold this position in the free flow of the breath for up to half a minute. Then bring the arms back into the basic posture of the scales and come out of the position.

With increasing practice, the movements become harmonious and graceful. The variations of the scales remind one of the lightness of a dancer. For the following position, now raise the leg up slightly off the ground. Let your spine grow upwards into the stretch. This position is easier than the basic position. Above all it gives a feeling of freedom which awakens through the floating, dancer-like lightness.

Headstand:

The scales is the best and most graceful preparation for the headstand. Although from its outer image this asana appears very different, the headstand is very similar to the strengthening character of the scales. In the scales, the body is actively stretched in length from the lower trunk. In the headstand the base of the movement is likewise in the lower trunk. The dynamic extends into the hips and gently continues into the thighs until it is lost in the relaxed calf muscles and ankles.

Do not practise the headstand with high blood pressure, with problems of the cervical spine, or with disorders of the eyes or ears. The headstand poses no problems for a healthy person. Only fear of the unusual, inverted posture and of falling, inhibits a natural approach to the movement. This fear, however, is not justified. If necessary, put some blankets around you, then you will fall gently.

Practice begins in the kneeling position. Interlock your fingers and with your forearms form an equilateral triangle on the floor. Place the crown of the head on the floor and keep the back of the head stably fixed with your hands. The centre of the head carries the major part of the body weight. Draw your legs up close to the body until the spine is straightened up vertically over the head. Either raise one leg first, following with the other, or better still, raise both legs bent, until they can finally be brought into the vertical position.

In the beginning you will often fall. With time, however, you will succeed effortlessly in this position and it will even become comfortable. Breathe lightly; do not consider the body as heavy, but rather as if it had no weight. The headstand is an asana which rests in itself without any effort.

Many healing effects are connected with this position. The entire trunk is stabilised. The total vitality increases. The lower back with the abdominal and pelvic regions represents the unconscious world of the will-energy. The dynamic starts out from the lower part of the spine. If you learn to do the scales, then the road to the headstand is no longer far. Practise these positions as often as possible and one after the other. They give you the necessary physical basis for an upright posture, for alertness and energy for life.

The expansiveness of the inner

In normal life one's attention flows constantly outwards through the senses. Thus for the consciousness the soul in the inner is in a sphere which cannot be grasped. In order to experience real happiness and undying peace, the spirit must dominate life. However, it is the other way around. The outer world, with its demands, dominates the inner.

If one closes one's eyes, one clearly feels the unrest of one's thinking. The consciousness is not free, but is occupied by the impressions of daily life. If one wants to calm down, then multitudes of thoughts are churned up. The consciousness cannot become conscious of itself, of the soul.

This cycle of exercises centres energies directly to the spine and into the spinal cord. This gives rise to the experience of one's own power and of calm. The student reaches far into the outer world; moves his arms sensitively into the sphere. He returns, lets his movements come to rest and immerses himself in the stillness of the inner world.

Always practise with mindfulness and sensitivity. The calm in the inner can only awaken when your life is in order in its outer circumstances. All of life reflects back on the practice of the exercises. Conflicts with others, anger, worries, hatred, fear of loss, and desires disturb the natural order and harden the soul-body. The gate to the innermost heart, which bestows the sublime joy of gratitude and the warming power of giving, opens when life in general is consciously and responsibly shaped. Make an effort therefore, for a peaceful attitude, for helpfulness, good-heartedness, brotherly love and religious appreciation. You will experience expansiveness in life and with this, find expansiveness in the innermost heart as well.

A harmonious movement is formed from the expansiveness of the consciousness. The sitting twist is one of the classical Yoga positions. It describes devotion and sensitivity. The movement is sensitively guided to a clear form in calm steps.

Begin in the kneeling position. Sit to the right of your legs on the floor and bring the left foot over the right knee. Carefully straighten up the spine. In order to make this straightening-up easier, it is recommended to support yourself with the left hand next to the body and to bend the right arm against the raised thigh. Whilst doing this, turn to the left.

Pay attention that your shoulders are level, relax them and remain like this in preparation until you sense a feeling of relaxation while being upright. Then reach along the leg with the right arm and take hold of the left foot. This position is called Ardha Matsyendrasana in Sanskrit, the half spinal twist. It could be further developed in numerous variations, often very demanding in terms of difficulty.

Hold this position on each side for about three minutes. Then return to the kneeling position again.

Now sit to the left of your legs on the floor and place the right leg over the left thigh. Both feet face backwards; the knees lie one on top of the other. Straighten the spine and the head right up and become conscious of yourself. Man was born out of infinity, and this infinity lives in the inner. Move the arms out wide and sense the sphere in space. Nowhere is there a boundary. Everything exists in eternal unity.

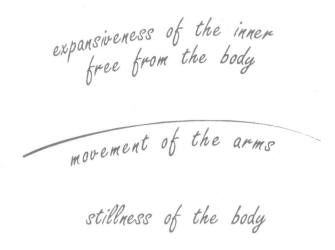

expansiveness of the inner

free from the body

movement of the arms

stillness of the body

Guide the right arm upwards out of the expansiveness and reach with the hand behind the shoulder. Also guide the left arm back out of the expansiveness and bring the hand to the right shoulder-blade. The fingers are clasped behind the back. Hold the head and the spine consciously upright. The wave of breath is allowed to flow freely (c.f. picture p.78).

In the inner lives the expansiveness of the whole universe. However, the inner is not a place, but an awareness of the infinity of life. The movement of the outer has come to a total standstill. Forget the tension in the arms as well, and lower your gaze into the boundless expansiveness of the inner. The breath comes and goes. It represents a silent connection to the outer sphere.

After some time, release this hand position again and sense into the expanse with your hands. The arms are the tools of the soul. The spine holds the head upright. Then guide the right hand to the left shoulder-blade and take hold of it from above with the left hand. Keep the eyes closed and hold the position again, in the consciousness of the inner expansiveness.

In Yoga this position is called Gomukhasana. It is the name for the face of a cow. The expansiveness of the inner is revealed in the gentleness and carefreeness of the face. The cow's face is a perfect example of this.

If you are not able to clasp the fingers behind your back, simply take hold of your sweater. A kneeling position can also be taken as an alternative leg posture. However, the position is then not as intensive energetically.

After finishing this exercise you can relax lying on your back. However, it makes sense to follow Gomukhasana directly with the inclined plane (exercise p.95) as a dynamic supplementary exercise.

The balancing head-knee pose

The balancing head-knee pose is perceived by most people as difficult and strenuous. In general, it is important in doing all the exercises, to practise with clear decisiveness. This is particularly true for this balancing position, which also demands a great willingness to stretch. Decisiveness in the exercises results in joy and success. The joy in physical activity is not perceived as an effort or strain. The right attitude towards practice leads to regeneration and constructive metabolic processes even while doing the asana.

Clear decisiveness leads to concentration in one's life. Insecurity, timidity, listlessness and tiredness, on the other hand, are the result of a lack of decisiveness and rob the whole individual, on a physical as well as on a soul level, of much strength.

In order not to apply strenuous force to the body in these balancing stretches, it is recommended to direct one's attention to the here and now and to begin with a clear intention. The body may start to sweat.

This balancing exercise is practised in three phases. The practice is completely safe. The first two phases can also be done by those who are less flexible.

Sit on the mat with your legs drawn up towards you. Put both hands around the feet with interlocked fingers. Balance on your buttocks. The knees point outwards. This open position, in which the back should already be upright, is the first phase.

Stretch the legs upwards in a dynamic movement until the knees are almost straight. The body is sensitively balanced in a narrow angle. This is the second phase of the exercise. It gives a pleasant sense of calm. Balance, strength and concentration are combined.

Now straighten up the spine in a decisive way and bring the head to the shins. Keep the legs as straight as possible. The shoulders should not be tensed up. The dynamic is applied more strongly in the lower back than in the shoulders. Let the breath flow lightly and in a free rhythm. This final phase of the exercise can even be held up to a few minutes. Plan a long holding-time. The balancing head-knee pose will give you joy, if you go into it intensively and decisively.

The shoulderstand

In colloquial language, the shoulderstand is also called the candle. The body rests on the shoulders, neck and upper arms. The trunk is ideally vertically upright like a candle.

Amongst all Yoga exercises, this posture takes the central position. It symbolises purity and female grace. The effects of the candle are gentle, but very deep-reaching. The female heart symbolises the deep power of perception, the unconditional love of others. An individual who is deeply founded in the heart, does not live according to sympathy or personal leanings, but directly out of the soul which provides warmth and security for the whole environment.

In daily life, man keeps his head and trunk upright. In the shoulderstand, however, this image is reversed. The abdomen is situated above the lungs and heart; the head rests motionless on the floor. This inversion causes a pleasant flow through and energising of the inner organs.

If one compares the human being to a plant, then through contemplative observation one gains the understanding of how the human being represents the counterpart of a plant. A plant is free of cravings, fear and unrest. Man, however, is busy, driven and possesses innumerable wishes and aims. He does not integrate himself into the rhythm of the seasons, but removes himself from the natural order through the power of his thinking and wanting.

In the shoulderstand, however, the individual becomes a silent flower. He keeps his head, which represents thinking and sense-perception in general, on the ground, just as the root of the plant rests in the earth. The respiratory system with the lungs and the heart, form the centre which is raised up above the head and shoulder-girdle. It corresponds to the leaves of the plant.

The abdomen is the seat of the human will-power. In this region the metabolic processes are at work and carry out all the constructive activity for the body. The abdomen corresponds to the blossom of a plant. Thus the human body in the shoulderstand is like a flower which strives towards the sky with its blossom, forms its centre with the leaves and is based in the earth with its roots.

The shoulderstand is one of the most important exercises for breathing. During its practice the wave of breath flows rhythmically and evenly into the depths of the abdomen. The entire digestive tract, the heart as well as the circulatory system are purified in a gentle way and the nerves are calmed. Resting completely and motionlessly in the posture with attention and devotion, brings about a gentle feeling in the heart organ itself. Devotion to an exercise leads the individual to purity and inwardness.

To practise this asana lie in the resting position with closed legs. Bring the legs up first and then the trunk. The hands then support the back with the elbows remaining as close together as possible. Raise yourself up with a gentle dynamic out of the thoracic spine, leaving, however, the legs, the abdomen and the shoulders relaxed. A subtle upright dynamic in the trunk is combined with the relaxation of the rest of the body. Hold the shoulderstand at first for one minute, then up to ten minutes or longer.

The shoulderstand is especially recommended for longer holding times. This asana will be very beneficial for a healthy body. With problems in the back, neck or head region you should work carefully. Caution is also called for with high blood pressure and the advice of a doctor should be sought.

Rising up into the complete vertical form should not be forced immediately. Through practising this position and also the other dynamic exercises the capacity develops to rest in the posture, upright while simultaneously relaxing.

A difficult variation is possible with the arms. Guide the arms upwards and place the hands on the thighs while at the same time keeping the back and legs straight.

During the shoulderstand, always allow the breath to flow freely and lightly.

The sitting position

The sitting position on the ground is natural in India. In those countries which are very strongly penetrated by the spirit of Yoga, it causes most people no difficulty at all.

For the harmony of the sitting position it is not so much the technique but far more the attitude of the soul which is significant. The image of a person sitting on the ground, silently devoted to meditation, creates a pleasant and graceful effect. The spine is vertically upright; the legs and arms rest motionless. The eyes remain either closed or unobtrusively opened. The natural character is revealed through the humility of this posture.

The sitting position on the floor is also recommended for the Westerner. During silent meditation or pauses for contemplation, subtle energies flow along the spine. Concentration increases with a consciousness out of the soul. The body rests on the ground. It is body. A religious perception in the heart, which appreciates the higher world of the spirit, leads to a feeling of freedom from the body. Thus the spine can be effortlessly straightened. The humility of the soul leads to harmony in the sitting position.

The simplest position is the kneeling position. Sit on the heels and place one hand in the other on the thighs. This position is recommended for beginners.

Advanced students should choose the cross-legged position. To make it generally easier, it is recommended to use a hard cushion or a folded blanket as an aid. By sitting with the buttocks slightly higher than the legs, the straightening-up of the spine also becomes easier. With increasing practice, it will eventually become possible to reduce the support or to do without it completely.

A very advanced sitting position is the half lotus. Pull one leg close to the inside of the thigh and bring the other foot over the shin into the groin. Keep the head upright.

The full lotus is the most perfect sitting position. It is recommended for all those who devote themselves with their souls more deeply to Yoga. The body rests very stably on the floor; the spine can be effortlessly straightened up. In this posture, attention and concentration increase. The closed form of the position provides a pleasant perception of calm. The image of a person in the lotus can be compared to an unobtrusive flower, which rests and at the same time remains open to the cosmic sphere of light. Place the right foot in the groin, paying attention that the right knee stays on the floor. Proceed gently and without force. Pull the left leg over the right to form a cross. Initially hold this position for a few minutes, until eventually you can remain in it without pain for up to fifteen minutes.

The sitting position in general should be practised as often as possible. The learning of the half or full lotus takes place as you delve into life's profound soul-mysteries. The greater the attentiveness towards the spiritual laws of life becomes, the more an inner will-power matures in the soul. The hip-joint, the flexibility of which is decisive for the lotus, becomes mobile through the inner will towards God. Reflect again and again upon the sublime significance of eternal life and upon the cosmic self. Thus the soul becomes familiar with the contents of the spiritual world. With knowledge and confidence in the sublime grace of eternal life, the capacity to stretch the body grows more and more. The sitting position on the floor will bring you joy. Even for Westerners it is the best position for meditation.

Stability and flexibility

The schooling of the breath is at the same time an active schooling of the body. The Yoga postures are very well-suited for this. For Westerners too, they are easy to learn. Through the work with the body the consciousness is awakened. One works from the tangible to the intangible.

A strenuous exercise of the body should not be exhausting as in sport, but should lead one to greater alertness and strength. The breath is always observed, but at the same time allowed to flow in its free movement. Concentration is involved in every phase of the exercise. One should always avoid working mechanically, as one then perceives one's limits more and more clearly and learns to use the body in a harmonious way.

The spine is particularly significant for a useful schooling. It should be flexible in all parts. The back muscles should also be so strong that an upright posture is effortlessly ensured. If there are blockages in the back, this affects the entire posture. With this the breathing is also diverted from its natural movement.

The image of the upright posture with the head erect shows an individual's self-confidence. The spine is the physical carrier of the soul-spiritual life. In it is shown the individual's own dynamic. If the spine is weakened or blocked in certain sections, then one's power to act in life is also weakened. As a result, many things in one's personal existence become more laborious and more difficult.

These exercises should promote flexibility on the one hand and stability on the other. With the strengthening of the back, all of the respiratory muscles are also strengthened. Thus the breath can flow more effortlessly and more fully. Without any of this active physical schooling, breath exercise would have very little long term success. Flexibility and stability in the spine form a secure foundation for healthy inner experience and for activity in life.

A tree which directs its branches high up towards the sky, puts out strong roots in the earth and is held by a solid trunk. In the same way an individual who develops in sensitive directions needs a strong backbone. This applies in an outer as well as in an inner sense.

These exercises can be practised individually, or also combined with others. Give yourself time and sense inwards while practising. A physical exercise is always simultaneously an exercise of consciousness. Practise resolutely, according to your ability; however, you should not be caught in achievement-orientated thinking.

The standing head-knee pose is above all a calming exercise. It promotes flexibility of the lower back and leads to a natural deepening of the breathing. Close the legs and let the upper body hang forwards. At this stage you should still not pull with the arms. Breathe consciously and let the shoulders, the head and the arms hang forwards in a relaxed way. Only after you perceive a feeling of calm and inwardness do you put a dynamic into the lower spine, thus pushing yourself slowly forwards so that the palms of the hands are finally flat on the ground. The end position, however, need not be reached immediately; it requires prolonged practice (c.f. picture p.73).

From this exercise you can develop a more difficult variation: Take hold

93

of the left ankle with the left hand, thus pulling yourself further down. The right leg is pushed high up behind you as a counter-movement. The farther you go into this active stretch, the faster the breathing becomes. Consciously hold the position for half a minute and then change to the other side. After practising, straighten up again and relax the upper body.

Backward-bending exercises: In a sense they represent a contrast to the head-knee positions. Take a sitting position with straight legs. The palms of the hands are placed a short distance behind the back on the floor. Actively stretch through the upper spine, opening the rib-cage wide forwards. The breathing remains free in its rhythm and in its movement.

With this exercise you can sense the thoracic spine and mobilise the individual parts of the spine better. Increase the tension and stretch the breastbone far forwards. With this the spine is stretched between the shoulder-blades. The further you stretch, the freer the breathing becomes.

From this active tensing in the back, raise the hips off the ground and support yourself entirely on your hands. The body forms an inclined plane. This is also the name of this posture. If it is easy for you, you can press the soles of the feet flat on the floor and go into the maximum possible stretch. Hold for a few seconds or up to one minute if possible. Through the intense input of strength the breathing becomes free and detached from the body.

The inclined plane strengthens the back, the shoulders and the arms. The freer breathing required through the high input of strength, vitalises the entire metabolism. This produces a pleasant, freeing effect. The front of the body is opened; deep breathing takes place more easily. The inclined plane is suitable after the head-knee pose as an equalising counter-movement.

If you already have a very strong and flexible back, then you can do the preparatory exercise for the diamond. The end position requires utmost strength in the spine and should only be attempted after a longer period of training (c.f. picture p.92).

Kneel up. The knees can be slightly apart. Direct the attention to the spine and stretch up towards the crown of the head. The hands can be placed on the thighs. Grow further and further upwards. From this stretch, the upper back can be bent further and further backwards. During this movement you must not feel any pressure in the lumbar region. The stretch through the spine must be so strong and precise in the thoracic region that the lower vertebrae are not compressed but are also stretched. As soon as you feel the lower back, you must stretch the rib-cage further upwards. This is how the intense continuous stretch is achieved. However, only go as far as is really possible.

This active tensing promotes thoracic breathing. The breathing capacity is expanded and deep breathing becomes easier. If the movement is easy for you, you can stretch further backwards; however you must use the muscles in the upper back powerfully. Always consciously maintain the tension and lie after practising in the relaxing position on your back.

The half diamond

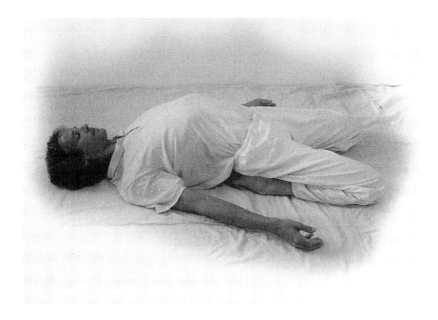

This sensitive position requires patience and attentive work. It is suitable to practise it after the backward-bending asanas. With its calm character it has a harmonising effect on the nervous system and as a result of the equal distribution of tension it increases the constructive metabolic processes.

The half diamond starts from the sitting position and ends lying on the floor. The student slowly adapts to the stretches taking place along the front of the body. He devotes himself to the new situation, as is directly shown in the image of the posture. The body does not elevate itself to greatness but bows to the approaching expansiveness. It becomes smaller and unobtrusive. The consciousness of inwardness and calm grows with increasing devotion. Finally the body rests without strain with the neck and head on the floor.

During the dynamic phase and also in the end position, the breath glides in very gentle waves. Devotion from the centre of the deep soul allows the breath to fade into the imperceptible. The entire musculature of the body becomes soft. Meditative feeling does not only change the consciousness, but the body too is gradually changed in its entire quality. Particularly backward-bending in devotion and attentiveness, leads one into the world of meditation. The higher, inspirative life rises above usual thinking. In a continuous, yet gradual way, the student approaches the higher spiritual goal. The entire body becomes permeable, just as a diamond is permeable to the light of the cosmos.

Begin in the kneeling position. Support yourself with your hands behind you. In a gentle way tense the spine. Slowly and attentively the way backwards begins. It must be emphatically stressed that under no circumstances must the spine kink. A gentle, continuous tension is constantly maintained. Continue to support yourself on your elbows and, if the stretch permits, place your head on the floor. Be constantly aware of the spine, however, and avoid a strong stretch through the neck.

With some persistence, you will eventually reach the end position. The head, the neck and the shoulders lie on the floor. The palms of the hands are turned upwards. Leave the breath in a gentle, natural movement and relax the thinking.

For the dynamic phase you will require some minutes. If you reach the end position, you can hold this for up to ten minutes in calm relaxation.

The relaxing position and deep breathing

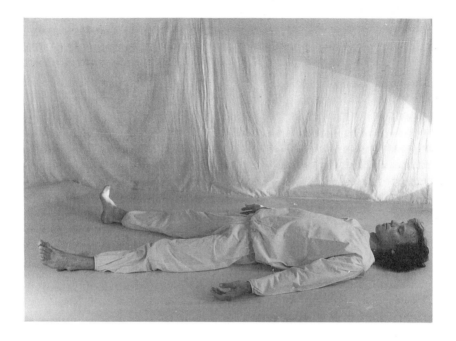

Relaxation means conscious letting go. The body is the symbol of the outer. It rests as if in deep sleep. Only the consciousness is alertly and actively involved in the exercise.

All breathing exercises as well as all Yoga postures and relaxation exercises are exercises of consciousness. So, too, is this relaxation. During its practice one gains a more or less clear perception of the transitory and the intransitory. Life, in its day-to-day events is plagued by alien impressions and thus the consciousness is distanced from actual inner reality.

The spirit is eternal. Earthly existence is subject to the laws of change and transience. Along with the body, one's outer existence is also released in this exercise. The thinking continues to flow as naturally as the whispering of the wind, and the will dissolves like a drop of water in the sea.

In the relaxing position, the student gains this consciousness of limit and limitlessness, and does not cling to a goal, but allows his whole person to sink.

The relaxing position is very important. It should be practised after all strenuous exercise cycles for a few minutes. It can also, however, be practised on its own as an actual exercise. It is particularly suited for all those who wish to find calm and composure in themselves. In this position, the subtle energies gather and concentrate in the interior. A good relaxation is more valuable than a deep sleep, as not only does the body regenerate, but the soul, too, gathers its forces. After practising, one feels mentally strengthened.

Relaxation is the prerequisite for inner experience. That natural joy out of the depth of the heart is the expression of outer release. Burdensome impressions are laid aside with the body. As long as there are tensions, as long as worries burden one's existence, no relaxation is possible. Only when there is readiness to let go does natural calm develop. So relaxation means recognition of the outer, transitory world. If this recognition is gained in the exercise, it leads to fearlessness and peace.

In order to achieve a real, deep relaxation, practice is necessary. Lie on a surface which is not too soft but also not too hard. Two blankets folded on top of one another are quite suitable. If you have practised a few active physical exercises beforehand, it is easier to find your way into the relaxation.

To practise, first take a sitting position with the legs drawn up towards you. In order to place the body symmetrically, the position of the spine is of great importance. Support yourself from behind with your elbows and move backwards vertebra by vertebra in a straight line.

Finally the back of the head touches the floor. Pay attention to the sacrum at the lower end of the spine. This bone should be felt resting evenly and securely on the floor. One by one let the legs slide along the blanket and turn the feet loosely outwards. The distance between the ankles is about thirty centimetres. If the legs are too close together, it is more difficult to relax the hips and the lower back.

In order to improve the position of the shoulders and the shoulder-blades once more, lift the fore-arms and touch the collar-bones with the fingers. This brings the elbows into a slight stretch and the shoulders are placed more evenly on the ground. Bring the fore-arms back down so that the palms of the hands fall upwards without tension.

This is the normal relaxing position. It is also called the corpse pose, as the body lies completely motionless. The pulse calms down; the breathing becomes slower. In this position the body needs no active muscle tension.

Concentration and deep relaxation are more easily found if the body lies symmetrically. Check your position once again therefore, so that you then no longer have to move. The head should also be in line with the spine, since if it tilts to the side, this leads to loss of concentration and sleepiness.

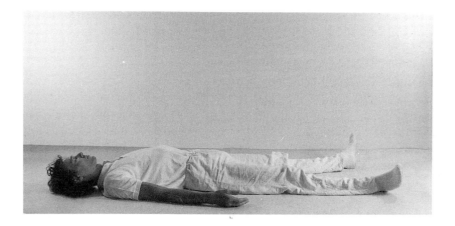

Consciously let go of the joints and the muscles of the legs. Mentally move through the body and relax all parts of the body from the feet upwards through visual imagination: the hips, the lower back, the abdomen, the middle back, the diaphragm, the upper back and the rib-cage, the shoulders, the arms, the hands and the fingers, the neck, the lower jaw, the jaw muscles, the face, the temples and the skin of the head.

As soon as a perception of calm and detachment has arisen, pay conscious attention to your will. Dissolve your will outwards. Imagine that your will leaves the body. Any thought of a goal disappears outwards. Just as a bird rises up in the air and flies towards the horizon, until it finally escapes one's view, so your will dissolves out of the body into infinity.

Gently turn your attention to the breathing. Let the concentration unfold from within, but avoid phases of dreaming or semi-conscious states. The breathing comes from outside and permeates you in your being. It is not subject to your own will, but comes and goes in its own movement, intensity and rhythm. Observe this breathing without interfering. It is clearly perceptible at the nostrils. The more you direct your attention inwards, the more you perceive its stream right into the deeper regions of the lungs.

Pay attention, however, that you do not tense the thinking. As soon as you hold on to a thought, the skin of your body tenses. This also brings the respiratory muscles into slight tension and the sensitive stream becomes harsher again.

Remain in this position, now, for at least five and up to twenty minutes. Through relaxation the breathing is deepened in a natural way. Observe the abdominal and pelvic regions. Let the breathing work entirely by itself. It is a greater force which approaches you from a far distance; it permeates and fills you with soft warmth. In guiding the attention to the various regions of the body, you also indirectly guide the breathing. If, for example, you observe the lumbar region, you can perceive how the gentle wave envelops this region.

You can also contemplate on an increased intensity of breathing. However, you must always accept the breathing as something greater. The more you achieve this idea, the more the breathing will lead to a consciousness of freedom.

In particular, the deep breathing gained in this way brings very great calm. It harmonises the metabolism and gives vitality and sound sleep. The heart is eased; the excretory system strengthened. Processes of ageing such as arteriosclerosis and premature symptoms of degeneration are thus considerably inhibited. If deep breathing is practised often, then with time it develops into an unconscious habit.

In this exercise the body prepares itself to receive the wave of breath unimpeded. The breathing works entirely by itself. This sensation is important and should be clearly perceived.

A process of consciousness is connected with this sensation. By letting go of his will in the exercise, the individual recognises the expansiveness of the breath. He becomes conscious of the source of life's tensions within himself. The body is not subject to one's will. With relaxation it is free, and attachments are also released. Thus the individual can recognise that all phenomena of life have a significance. This newly gained knowledge helps towards appreciation of the inner impulse.

For relaxation, it is particularly important that the consciousness is always kept awake. If one falls asleep or sinks into phases of dreaming, one does not recognise oneself in the exercise and the actual learning process does not take place.

A soul exercise

An exercise in which the attention is devoted for a certain time to a concrete matter, to an object or an idea, is an exercise of the soul or of the consciousness. Through devotion, calm and inwardness arise. The thinking is separated from the life of the wishes and the will. This subtle separation leads to new insights and impressions. The soul reveals itself as a being of light.

As long as the thinking is connected with the personal wish-life, a certain unrest in the mind and a feeling of attachment to the body prevails. As far as one can talk of an aim in the consciousness-exercises, this consists in re-orienting the thinking, in making it more full of light. Through attaching the thinking to the wishes, it becomes heavy. The freedom of the thoughts from one's own personal needs enables a wide, unlimited view. The soul separates itself from the attachment to the body and becomes receptive for the high spiritual truths.

It is important for the soul-exercise that one devotes oneself with one's attention to a matter, an object or a person without expecting any benefit. Usually the thinking always tends towards those matters from which it anticipates the greatest benefits. However it is important to set oneself concrete tasks, independent of one's own wishes, which lead to objective insights.

For the evening, a consciousness-exercise is suitable which leads one to better digest the impressions and events of the past day. The exercise can most simply be done by tracing back through the events in a coherent sequence. Here it is important not to anticipate a benefit for oneself, but to observe the events quite neutrally. The thoughts become lighter and ordered. Through repetition of the exercise, you will develop an entirely new gift of observation and greater attention for your fellow men.

Sit on the floor in an upright sitting posture. Now observe the past day, tracing backwards. Inwardly let the events run before you once again like a film rolling backwards. Quite consciously keep the reversed sequence and observe the various people whom you met during the day. You will notice how little real attention there was for your fellow men.

Furthermore you will get a feeling for the reality of a higher guidance in the whole of life. You yourself, as well as all others, are subject to this guidance.

This contemplative soul-exercise should be practised regularly for a period of around ten minutes. It is suitable for the evening as it leads one once again to a perception of one's fellow men. The reversed sequence is important in order to give the thinking a completely different impulse.

This soul-exercise has very positive effects on sound sleep. A consciousness for one's fellow men, founded in the soul, leads one to fall asleep in a pleasant way. The cause of sleeplessness very often lies in being fixed on one's personal wishes. If the consciousness is directly strengthened and open to one's fellow men, then these difficulties in falling asleep disappear.

Pranayama –
the spiritual school of life

Literally translated, Pranayama means "control of the life-force". Life and growth is only possible through energy. This energy, however, is not visible to the eye because it belongs to the subtle body of man. However, this energy permeates and sustains all life on this earth. In Yoga it is known as Prana. In Japan and China, the countries from which acupuncture comes, the same energy is called chi and in the Western world one calls it electromagnetic energy.

This energy flows continuously through man. It is active in all parts of the body. In some regions it is more strongly active; in other parts less so. It has a decisive meaning for the whole of life. So this energy determines one's physical health and, from a wider perspective, the state of the soul as well as the consciousness.

Pranayama is a special form of breathing. Pranayama is an important limb in the physical and spiritual school of Yoga. By guiding the breath in a certain way, one affects the subtle energy system. One leads the energy into specific regions of the body. Through holding the breath, one centres the energy in various organs and towards the spine. Every region of the body has a specific meaning for life and for the unfolding of the consciousness. With Pranayama, the possibility is given for deep-reaching changes in the body and in the consciousness.

Practice of these exercises must not be taken on lightly. Detailed knowledge of their effects is absolutely necessary, as these exercises have long-term consequences even after a short period of practice.

Rhythmatising the breath

The breathing is subject to a continuous rhythm. This rhythm in turn has a certain ratio with the pulse; about one to four. Spiritual science research documents report of the great world rhythm. In one day an individual breathes 25,920 breaths. The zodiac, through the astral influences, symbolises the physical and spiritual development of man. With the unconscious rhythm of breathing, the entire development of the individual is embedded in the universal law of life.

Rhythm is of particular significance in life, as all phenomena on earth are subject to a rhythmical process. The entire plant and animal kingdom is subject to changing and repeating laws. Winter goes and summer comes. Nothing escapes the great rhythmical event. The organs of man also work in rhythmic activity. In the great as in the small, there is rhythm. That which is visible in individual details continues in the infinite world of the cosmic.

A constantly working rhythm determines the development of the earth and with this the development of man. Thus one is subject to a great law; rhythm rules man.

Through the power of self-knowledge, it is possible for man to interfere with the autonomous rhythm of breathing. This, now, is the case with Pranayama, the Yogic breathing. The inhalation and exhalation is consciously prolonged. At the peak of the inhalation, the breath is also held in a pause. In this way, the natural, unconscious breathing rhythm is altered by means of a longer, conscious rhythm.

Now in order to understand the effects of this conscious alteration, one must observe the significance of breathing from a holistic perspective. The breathing guides the individual with a specific rhythm. It determines the well-being of his soul and influences the thought-life. Every human being has an individual quality of breath and an individual rhythm. Out of the interaction of the outer environmental conditions with the predispositions of the person, the particular structure of the individual being is formed. This structure receives its determination through the breathing. So the breathing works as a greater power in man and guides him through life.

Now the Pranayama student alters the rhythm of inhalation and exhalation and also shapes the quality of the stream of breath more precisely and delicately. The autonomous process is consciously experienced and at the same time is also altered. This has decisive effects on the entire shaping of life and unfolding of the personality, as from far away, the rhythm guides man in his existence.

In life man unconsciously allows himself to be guided by the forces of the breath. He trusts in the natural order and gives himself to the guidance. Now in Pranayama, however, he takes the reins into his own hands and begins to steer his forces. By changing the rhythm of the breathing, he affects his subtle body and with this shapes himself a new existence from within.

With Pranayama one begins to determine one's life and one's life-goal. Great responsibility is taken on with this self-determining, as man cannot live life without a goal. He requires a precise map of his path, otherwise he roams about in ignorance and drives his strength to exhaustion and misjudges his potential.

Pranayama means conscious guidance of the breath and with this, conscious shaping of life. Whoever interferes with the autonomous rhythm, alters his being and takes great responsibility upon himself, as one removes oneself consciously from worldly events and from the natural order of things. The law of cause and effect, which rules over the path of life, is, through targeted breathing exercise, now declared invalid. The breathing rhythm connects the physical body with the life of the soul in a uniting way. This unity is experienced through Pranayama on a higher level. Thus the individual raises himself; he frees himself from the shackles of earthly attachment.

Pranayama can only be understood in a spiritual sense. It does not serve as therapy for illness or mental imbalance, but rather the consciousness is raised to a spiritual dimension. This path requires a high degree of self-responsibility and must not be lightly undertaken.

In this schooling of the breath there lies a great danger. He who practises the exercises over a period of some weeks will notice that his whole life changes. A quite specific power awakens within the personality, and one does not yet really know where it will lead. Many new things are discovered in life. Moods and feelings change; one's temperament becomes calmer. Deep within, the student senses, that with Pranayama he can gather more and more strength within his being. This also gives him the sense that with this he can grow beyond his possibilities and limits; indeed he notices that he can even grow beyond nature. By continually expanding his consciousness through the breathing, he obtains more power, as he sees more and understands more. His being is opened to sensitive impressions; however at the same time he is also more vulnerable. The longer one practises Pranayama, the more one alters one's entire personality.

One needs a great deal of stability, knowledge and life-experience to also be able to use the forces of Pranayama in a truly meaningful way. If the awakened forces are not used, they have a destabilising effect on the entire life of the individual. It can even go so far that feelings of fear and isolation arise.

The path of Pranayama must only be started if the individual has already found contentment and happiness in his personal sphere. He must carry love in his heart. He must be ready to be able to serve and his personal circumstances must be in order. The great responsibility of self-determining can only be taken on with experience and maturity. Life, within one's personal fields, must be free from earthly demands.

The actual task of Pranayama schooling lies within life itself. The rhythmatising of the breath in the exercises only gives the basis for subsequent understanding and action. A path should be shaped from within. Everyday-life, however, is not changed.

With the schooling of the breath in Pranayama, one's outer existence is not to be changed, but rather one's inner attitude and the relationship to one's fellow men is to be purified in a loving way. A path is consciously travelled from within, out towards others. The ethical laws, as they are taught in the classical writings of Yoga or in other spiritual disciplines, are of no valuable help for this, as through them the student does not quite find that connection to others which is necessary to meaningfully apply the forces of Pranayama for spiritual development. In them, only rules of conduct are described, but no paths towards a common spiritual unfolding.

Over and above the ethical rules of a pure life, the Pranayama student must actively work for a relationship to his fellow men. The breath-exercises only serve to gather energy. The further path of the schooling is actively shaped in the outer world.

In order to understand the effect of Pranayama exercises, one can observe the image of the exercise. The student rests in a tightly locked sitting position and contemplates with attention deeply on his being. He enters entirely into his world. Everything external is released for the duration of the exercise; the yardstick is sought within his own being. No movement disturbs the silence. The student guides the breathing so tenderly and evenly that an outsider can hardly hear it. The more he experiences this calm and seclusion within and the more concentration he gathers, the less air he needs. His breathing rhythm can become extremely long.

From this exercise one can see that it serves to gather forces. An incredibly high level of concentration can thus be reached. However, one cannot banish the soul into oneself; one must then move outwards, out of oneself again. The strength gained should be applied in a way that is meaningful for life and for one's fellow men.

Pranayama exercises are very intensive and deep-reaching. They are much more effective than all other physical Yoga exercises. Man possesses the driving powers of thinking, feeling and wanting. If the breathing rhythm is altered and the breath is held, then these soul-powers are grasped in a particular way. The breathing and the soul-powers are connected to each other. By slowly and deeply drawing the air into himself, holding it and finally releasing it in a long stream, the student also gathers the soul-powers. He draws the powers of thinking deep into his inner, but also draws his feeling and his wanting from the outer into the inner. In the inner space there is now no boundary. Everything appears in a dissolved form. The soul-powers of thinking, feeling and wanting blend together in the expanded space of the inner. Just as one pours different colours together and thus obtains a new shade, one blends the soul-powers with each other and thus in turn obtains a certain relationship to the outside. This is a newly shaped capacity of the powers which leads life into different orbits.

When the eyes are opened again after the exercise and the gaze is directed outwards, the student is changed in his consciousness. His being is more compact, more closed. The powers are centred and therefore calm and stable. Lively, subjective perception determines the consciousness. A change has taken place in the entire personality through the rhythmatising of the breath.

Now the individual must also apply these powers in a meaningful way, otherwise they will destroy him. So practising Pranayama means conscious shaping and guiding of life. The new consciousness is reflected in the relationship to others. Powers of knowledge have grown; thinking is clear and intimately connected with feeling. Through active shaping of life, these powers should be stabilised on a higher plane.

With Pranayama, the individual does not only take responsibility for himself, but also for all friends, relatives, acquaintances; for all those with whom he has contact. By contemplating inwards during the exercise, he experiences in himself that spiritual power which he must direct outwards again in his relating to others.

"Tat-tvam-asi". Thou art that. In this way a Sanskrit sentence describes this fundamental significance. Souls are connected with each other in the inner. One recognises the other, sees him, feels him, experiences him. Such recognition leads to deep understanding and the great longing for spiritual development is quenched through this active understanding of others. A bridge is created from one's own "I" to the other, and this bridge brings that consciousness of unity and connectedness that the path of Yoga describes.

The path of spiritual development is a path of love. Pranayama serves as a source of power for this path, but love is not to be understood as a demand. It springs from the heart and contains responsibility, caring, empathy and wisdom. It must not be forcefully imposed, just as Pranayama exercises must not be practised with the compulsion to achieve spiritual perfection.

The effect of Pranayama is tied to experience. That which grows out of the exercises is of a tremendous nature. Thinking, feeling and wanting are guided deep inside. If the individual were to remain fixed in these areas, he would soon lose his orientation in his inner space. The expansiveness would make him frightened and forlorn. After the exercise one must consciously turn towards to life again.

The first point in the school of Pranayama is to recognise and to experience in the outer. In everyday consciousness we as people are very different from one another through our thinking and feeling; however in the inner we are connected. This inner is now quite consciously carried to the outside and a sensitive experience should touch the perception. Every individual carries a soul within himself. This soul lives in the body. The body is visible; the soul invisible. Only through very deep immersion with expansion of the consciousness can one behold the soul. For this the sense-life must become quite still, clear and calm. The first point in the schooling of Pranayama should lead to this stillness and clarity. Thus the student gains a slight notion of the soul and with this an experience of unlimitedness awakens.

He cannot see this inner, but he can prepare his consciousness for sensitive receptiveness. The more one occupies oneself with the thought of the soul which lives in the body, the more one will open the consciousness. Sensitive receiving begins. This is a tremendous task for the student, as with it a great demand to learn begins. That which was prepared in the inner through conscious breathing, is now concretely shaped as an exercise on the outside.

So self-knowledge is to know of the soul in others. Thinking is a driving power which outwardly steers life in a determining way and inwardly occupies the consciousness through the various trains of thought. With Pranayama exercises, the student detaches himself from the heaviness of all impressions and thus becomes wide-awake and clearly present. The consciousness is opened. Lovingly and receptively, the student prepares himself for the environment. He does not only perceive the surface, but also the reality of forces and that which is essential. His thinking should remain receptively open to the outside, so that he consciously holds back his "I" and receives the other, recognising and understanding him.

In the world which shows itself beneath the visible threshold as a separate reality, there is no separation or limitation. Only the will of one's own "I", which advances into the environment, and the thought which reveals itself, rising above the soul, brings separation. Life is manifold and as long as outer actions and aimless thoughts determine one's existence, there is no unity. Thus one must learn to distinguish between the essential and the inessential. The student must not interfere with the nature of others with his thinking and ways of acting. He must direct his attention towards his receptive side and first perceive the greater working of inner existence. If he pushes into the world with his actions or with his speech, he disturbs that divine working of the inner and will thus receive no further guidance. The infinity of his soul becomes overshadowed and he experiences himself again as an individual being, separated from others. Contentedness and happiness in life exist in the consciousness of unity and connectedness. This unity is experienced out of the innermost regions.

Loving, outwardly directed activity is the actual purpose of spiritual schooling. Life, as the most valuable thing, is preserved through correct listening and thus deep understanding. This is not passivity, but rather highest activity of the consciousness. The student does not need to force himself to be silent, but must only observe that inner law of the soul and thus bring about harmony and peace in his environment.

Self-realisation is not possible without other people. The divine thought of the immortal soul is consciously experienced through close connection with one's fellow men. Joy and happiness will enrich that Pranayama student who allows all others to partake of his path. The outer phenomenon is experienced and penetrated with an inner thought. So the student experiences the closeness of the spirit and senses the inner connection to his fellow men.

True joy and true contentment are always connected with deep gratitude towards life. The receptiveness of the consciousness is one of the first stages of spiritual development. The further the student now walks on this path, the more difficult does it become for him to deal with his own "I". The active process of development does not take place in outer life, but occurs within the deep regions of the personality. Thus the path can no longer be influenced by outer wanting. Spirit is infinite; spirit is without beginning and without end; spirit is without goal.

In Yoga ashrams where Pranayama is taught, there is always a teacher present who instructs the student and assigns him the correct tasks. The student submits unconditionally to this teacher, as he knows that he can trust him and at the same time he also knows that without him he would not manage on his spiritual path.

This reflects a fundamental difference between Western and Eastern consciousness. Unconditional self-surrender is possible only for the fewest in our culture. Therefore for the Westerner, a different demand is associated with Pranayama. The student must reflect deeply upon life, and above all must become conscious of his own wanting. Anything that can be achieved through Pranayama can only be of a spiritual nature. He started the path to the spiritual wilfully, and now he has to give up his will again entirely. He must dedicate all his gained strength to life. Just as a student in the ashram submits unconditionally to a teacher, so the Pranayama student now submits unconditionally to life.

Life as love is always the victor, and there is nothing in the whole of existence which is greater than love. In order to make real progress on the path of

Pranayama, the student must submit to this love. He must not be plagued by outer wanting. From the innermost, he worships the greatness of the universe and lives in the stream of becoming and passing away, without clinging to an earthly goal. This does not mean that he should now no longer do anything; rather he should act, but should not want to possess; he should work but should not want to dominate; he should speak but should not want to impress with his speech. As he feels life as the most valuable treasure in himself, he now devotes himself with his whole being to that which has true existence. This is the submission which leads him to the actual goal of life. It is not a strenuous or extreme state. The consciousness of love is present. He experiences himself in joyful connection with others and thus also with the great event of existence. Humility and gratitude in life grow through the submission of one's own "I"-will to the cosmic will.

The fourth point on this path of schooling represents the entire framework of the preceding steps. The seeker often lacks orientation and also security on this path of self-determination and self-realisation. His being is open and his understanding of the sensitive areas of life grows. He schools his thinking and also his will so that he can thus establish an inner connection to his fellow men. Through Pranayama exercises, and through particular care of his soul, his whole personality becomes more vulnerable. Whoever practices for some time, very soon notices that he loses a certain protective covering, and now openly faces the impressions of life with his whole being. Thus he has to develop a power within himself which gives him a frame of orientation and also stability.

This power is entirely within himself and can be described as an inner voice. Within every individual, there lives the ability for true discrimination and true knowledge, only many feelings and thoughts get mixed into the perception-life of the soul. As a result one does not hear one's "own voice" correctly and is thus insecure in facing life and its everyday occurrences.

If, however, one listens quite silently into one's own being and trusts in one's own perception, this gives security and knowledge. In every individual an "inner voice" is revealed through perception. However, in order to receive the right answer from within, the feelings and thoughts must be silent. Feeling is bound to desire; the intellect to preconceived opinions. Only perception in the depths can reveal clarity and thus also truth. Thus the Pranayama student should make a particular effort to develop this perception so that he strengthens his own ability for discrimination and expands his sphere of knowledge. This gives him individual strength and self-confidence on his path. It also helps him to travel his own personal path.

As the final point in the schooling of Pranayama, the student must observe that on this path there is no return. He pulls up the draw bridge behind him. For whoever interferes intensively with the autonomous process of breathing, interferes with his life and therefore must also guide it himself. The way back to former ways of life remains barred.

The student detaches himself from old, formed impressions and gains new breadth of vision in the whole of life. This leads him directly into idealistic striving. Step by step he strides into a new world. He very quickly gains distance from past days. He must be ready to live a life for love. Thus one should not pursue this path without careful consideration. One must be conscious that one binds one's wishes to the divine goal and thus gives up one's life, in the sense of one's own wanting.

Practical aspects

Pranayama is the breath school of Yoga. You should acquaint yourselves with the teachings of Yoga before you begin with Pranayama. It is important to master the various asanas, the physical postures of Hatha Yoga. In doing this you prepare the body for the intense, deep-reaching effect of Pranayama.

Physical exercises (asanas) strengthen the respiratory muscles and give the spine support and suppleness. As long as there are blockages in the body, Pranayama makes no sense.

The first two exercises described here can also be practised by beginners. For the Pranayamas with breath retention and bhandas, a teacher who has a precise knowledge of these things should be found, for instruction and supervision.

Do not practise Pranayama with less than 21 years of age. This would interfere too intensively with the development of the personality.

Avoid Pranayama in all kinds of depression, mental worries, fluctuations of the mind and mood. Here the exercises of the free breath school are a valuable help. They give balance and harmony to the state of the soul.

Also refrain from practising Pranayama with feverish colds. Rhythmatising the breath serves to expand the consciousness. The nerves become more perceptive and thus one's whole sensitivity increases. So Pranayama only brings success in a balanced mental state and in physical well-being.

Always take enough time for an exercise so that you are not faced with everyday demands immediately afterwards. A contemplative pause should be held before and after the practice of an exercise.

Before you decide upon the more intense Pranayamas, read the chapter about their background several times. The points given must absolutely be observed. They are intended as a guide-line on this path. At present there is much literature on Pranayama exercises, as the teaching of Yoga is one of the most important paths of spiritual schooling. Almost all of the books describe the technique, but not the effects and deep background of the practice. They are therefore basically valuable for checking the technique, but not as a path in themselves.

Pranayama exercises should never be performed mechanically. A profound experience is always connected with the breathing. The path of schooling cannot be seen as a growth in stages into a different consciousness. Through activity and conscious relating to others and to nature, the depth of life is experienced with inner involvement. Pranayama brings a meditative consciousness. It alters the subtle body and builds up the physical body differently through the retention of carbon dioxide. It is penetrated with a gentle power. Pranayama can only be understood through feeling deeply into life's interconnections.

You must determine the time for Pranayama yourself. Early or late morning, afternoon or early evening are all suitable. Pranayama should not be practised too late as the thinking no longer has freshness and the subtle perception can thus no longer be so well used. It can also lead to difficulties in sleeping.

You can practise Pranayama one to three times a day. Choose a Pranayama which suits your personal possibilities.

Only one Pranayama exercise is described here: Nadi Shodhana Pranayama – alternate nostril breathing. Besides this exercise there are numerous further variations. The exercise described here is fundamental and is therefore taken as an example for the path of spiritual schooling of Pranayama. For further study, the various writings of the great and well-known Yoga masters are suitable.

Simple rhythmatising

This exercise can be practised by everyone as a simple equalising exercise. It requires some discipline, but no direct physical strain as it is performed lying down. The breath is combined with a movement. Thus one learns to prolong the duration of each inhalation and exhalation. It is a preparatory exercise for the actual Pranayamas.

The right side of the body corresponds to activity; the left more to passivity. In the astral sphere, sun and moon describe these two polar opposites. The entire body can be differentiated according to this division: upper and lower; inner and outer; front and back. So for example, the forwardly directed chest region corresponds to the sun side; the spinal cord with its nerve cords to the moon side. The heart lies in the centre of the chest region and is always actively working. It is the sun organ. The nerves, on the other hand, carry the sensory stimuli to the brain; they are of a receptive nature. They correspond to the moon or passive side.

The breathing affects the subtle body. It influences the energetic streams and thus creates certain conditions in the body and in the state of mind. If the stream of air flows harshly, the muscles become hard and tense up. If the stream becomes smooth and deep, relaxation occurs. If the rhythm is irregular and interrupted due to thinking that is burdened with worries, the nerves are strained. An even flow of breath leads to equilibrium, alertness and mental strength. Therefore this simple rhythmatising is suitable as a preparation for Pranayama.

Lie down on your back. The body should lie evenly and in a straight line on the floor. Close the legs and turn the palms of the hands to the floor next to your thighs. Relax the abdomen, the diaphragm and the shoulder girdle so that the breath finds its way in deeply without resistance.

Direct your attention to the right side of the body. The left side should be entirely forgotten. As far as possible, work only with the muscles of the right side. Breathe out and count to eight or ten in one-second intervals, lifting the right leg up straight. Breathe in again and lower the leg, counting to eight or ten again.

Repeat this movement ten times, one immediately after the other. You should pay attention to an even, deep and smooth flow of breath.

The same rhythm must always be kept. If the lifting of the leg is accompanied by an out-breath, then the lungs are freed from residual air and the new inhalation finds its way more easily into the depth. If one were to reverse the breathing and the movement, then the co-operation of the respiratory muscles would be adversely affected.

After finishing on the right side, change to the left. Direct the whole of your attention into the left side of the body and perform the movement the same number of times and in the same rhythm as on the right. The opposite, resting leg should remain relaxed throughout. The strength is drawn from the abdominal muscles.

After finishing the exercise, take the normal relaxing position. Gently tilt the pelvis and feel the individual lumbar vertebrae on the ground. Then let go and relax.

This exercise leads to greater calm and freshness in thinking. It can be performed at any preferred time.

Advanced students can leave a pause in breathing for a few seconds after breathing out. Here the leg is held up and the calmness of the inner space is felt. This brings about a sensitising effect in the nervous system.

Alternate nostril breathing without bhandas

This breathing exercise is called Nadi Shodhana Pranayama. It has a purifying effect on one's subtle body. One can develop this exercise from a very simple form up to the highest perfection. Progress is only possible gradually and slowly. The simple form, without breath retention, has no great consequences and can therefore be practised by healthy people without any danger.

In alternate nostril breathing, one breathes alternately and rhythmically through each nostril. This has an equalising effect on the energy system and leads to inwardness and calm. The building-up and breaking-down processes of the metabolism are brought into better balance. The left nostril is connected with the right hemisphere of the brain and is assigned to the moon. The right nostril is connected with the left hemisphere and is assigned to the sun.

Thus breathing into the left side brings more inner creative power, receptivity and passivity; breathing into the right side, on the other hand, brings more activity, power to execute matters, courage and heat. If one breathes through both nostrils alternately, general harmony and balance arise.

Every region on the periphery of the body has a connection to the inner organs and these in turn are connected with the consciousness. The outer can be perceived with the senses; the inner remains hidden in inaccessible layers. One feels the skin; one does not feel the organs. If one directs one's attention to the nose, one notices the gentle stream of air. At the entrance to the nostrils there are fine receptors which have a relation to the world of the inner organs. For Pranayama, the conscious flow of breath through the nose is therefore very important. Through it one can tune the breathing more sensitively and can exert an influence on deeper layers of the body.

Pranayama is always performed in a sitting position. The lotus is best suited, but causes most people difficulties. The half lotus or the cross-legged position are also possible. With these you should make sure that the knees are placed as near to the ground as possible. If the knees point up too high, then the spine can only straighten up with great strain. The abdomen cannot be properly freed from constriction. Simply place as many cushions as necessary under the buttocks until the knees touch the floor.

Straighten up the spine from base to top, vertebra by vertebra, as if you were erecting a perfectly straight tower. If the back still shows a curve in the thoracic region, breathing cannot take place to its full extent. The exercise then does not lead to an increase in energy, but soon leads to tiredness and listlessness.

Bring the shoulders back so that the chest is opened forwards. You should be able to feel your shirt against the front of the body; at the back it should only lie quite loosely against the skin. In this sitting position relax the jaw, the jaw muscles and the skin of the face.

Form a finger posture with your right hand. The thumb, ring finger and little finger are extended; the index and middle finger are bent into the hand.

This hand posture is a mudra which, translated, means "seal". This gesture with the hand is meant to indicate a certain inner attitude. Each finger has a meaning. The thumb symbolises the universal self; the ring finger the heart. However, this hand posture is also chosen for practical reasons. Once one has got used to it, one can regulate the breath flow at the nostrils much more gently than with any other hand posture.

With this finger posture, bring the right hand to the nose and leave the arm bent at the side of the rib-cage without tension. Place the thumb on the right nostril, the ring finger on the left. With gentle pressure, narrow the openings of the nostrils, sensing the free flowing of the breath in and out.

Consciously relax the abdomen as well as the shoulders and arms. The breathing should find its way easily and without resistance into the depth. Avoid any force. Wilful pressure should be avoided both in breathing in and in breathing out, as it burdens the nervous system and brings the thinking into increased tension.

Completely close the right side and breathe out through the left side, gently and fully. Once the lungs feel empty, breathe in through the left side in an even flow. The abdominal and lumbar region should offer as little resistance as possible to the breathing. Close the left nostril with gentle pressure of the ring finger and breathe out through the right side. When the lungs are empty, breathe in through the right side again, consciously and evenly. This is one round of alternate nostril breathing. Always continue like this: out left, in left, out right, in right, etc.

In order to achieve an even rhythm, you must count with every breath out and in. To begin with, choose a rhythm of five seconds breathing in and ten seconds breathing out. After some time this can be increased. Ten seconds breathing in and twenty seconds breathing out is the upper limit. You should not go further without special instruction.

Practise this exercise for about ten minutes, always guiding the breath consciously as well as gently. If it becomes strenuous, too strong a rhythm has been chosen. The more gentle and relaxed the flow of breath, the more the inner organs are released.

Keep the eyes closed throughout the entire exercise. The attention should be directed entirely to the breath so that you have the sensation that you yourself are the breath. The eyes should only be opened when you check the sitting posture.

In a gentle way this exercise calms the thinking. The receptivity of the soul is increased. After practising, allow some time before you start working. The calmness gained should be consciously sensed for a few more minutes.

For advanced students, a further step can be added to this simple form of alternate nostril breathing. After every inhalation, close the nose with the thumb and ring finger and hold the breath. You can gradually increase the duration of holding, starting with a few seconds. However, you should not hold for longer than twenty seconds.

A sensible rhythm is five seconds breathing in; ten, fifteen or twenty seconds holding and ten seconds breathing out again. During the breath retention, sense inwards and let the thinking stream by like the fine murmuring of the wind. Practise this exercise for ten to fifteen minutes.

Even this exercise has very deep-reaching effects and should only be practised by advanced students. Through the breath retention, energies are more intensely centred in the organs. This not only increases the receptivity for impressions of the soul, but even leads to changes in the nervous and sensory systems. All impressions are received and processed in a meditative way. As the energetic effect does not only take hold of the surface of the person, but reaches right down into the unconscious depths of the organs, the individual opens himself more intensely with his whole being and at the same time goes unprotected into the field of impressions and experiences of life.

Alternate nostril breathing with bhandas

This more developed form of Nadi Shodhana Pranayama must only be practised by very advanced students. It requires a very strong body, as complete breathing in and out takes place. The student makes use of all his respiratory muscles and fills the lungs from the depth of the abdomen right up to the tips in the collarbone area.

Bhandas are special, body-orientated exercises. Translated, Bhanda means "lock". The student applies specific muscular contractions in order to give a direction to the subtle energy. Both the complete inhalation and the retention of breath with bhandas demand disciplined practice. One usually needs a few weeks or even months to learn the right technique.

Two essential force poles determine the life of man. In Yoga these are called Shiva and Shakti. Shiva is the force of heaven, or the carrying force of creation. It is assigned more to the masculine side. Shakti on the other hand, is more the feminine pole or the earth force. It is symbolically depicted in the form of a serpent. This serpent is coiled three and a half times and rests at the lower end of the spine. As soon as spiritual development begins, the serpent awakens. It makes itself felt with its energy in the body through various changes which also affect the mind and consciousness.

Shiva is the immovable force, according to Indian mythology. It rests in the top of the skull. It is the consciousness; the everlasting, unchangeable "I" of man. Shakti on the other hand is mobile. It is called the Kundalini force. In the practice of Pranayama, one gathers energy and with the bhandas keeps hold of this energy inside. One produces a conscious congestion. Heat surges up as a result, and this heat awakens the sleeping serpent at the lower end of the spine. It ascends with its energy directly within the spine, in the central nerve canal. At the top of the head it meets Shiva. Shiva is the father of creation. This uniting of Shiva and Shakti brings the uniting of all polarities. For man this means cosmic consciousness.

Pranayama exercises originate from a very ancient time. At that time their meaning and thus their application was different from today. For present-day man, the awakening of Kundalini Shakti would be a disastrous matter. With Pranayama, one should merely strive for a centring of the soul powers. The student reflects inwards; experiences the depth of his being. He gathers all powers and thus becomes able to raise inner life over and above outer life, so that the spirit permeates his practical life; so that the spirit determines his thinking and acting.

Before you begin with the practice of this demanding Pranayama exercise, you should first practise the two most important bhandas on their own: Jalandhara Bhanda is the chin lock. After complete inhalation, pull the chest even further up and lower the chin onto the breastbone. The stability in the middle of the back should not be lost. Do not force the chin downwards, but rather approach the chin with the breastbone. If contact is not possible, then for the time being just do the movement as far as is possible without over-exertion in the neck.

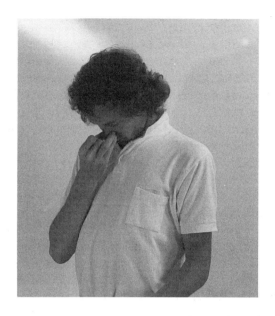

Mula Bhanda is the root Bhanda: After breathing in, contract the pelvic floor and pull the lower abdomen slightly inwards. You should thus prevent energy from escaping through the lower openings of the body. Mula Bhanda should not be a strenuous tensing, but a purposefully focussed contraction of the muscles which surround the pelvic floor.

Take the lotus or cross-legged position. The back should be carefully straightened up vertically. Bring the thumb and the ring finger to the nose (as in simple alternate nostril breathing) and narrow the nasal passages with gentle pressure. Leave the elbow by your side and direct your gaze inwards. Breathe out on the left until the lungs feel empty.

Breathe in on the left, guiding the air in an even stream first into the lumbar region, then into the upper abdomen, further into the sides, finally into the rib-cage and tips of the lungs. Direct your attention to the skin of your back and let this stretch expansively with the inhalation. This helps you to open the floating ribs at the bottom of the rib-cage and to guide the breath harmoniously over from the abdomen into the chest area. The inhalation is a conscious opening of the lungs. When the lungs are filled, pull the rib-cage up and lower the chin into Jalandhara Bhanda. Contract the muscles at the pelvic floor into Mula Bhanda. Hold the breath.

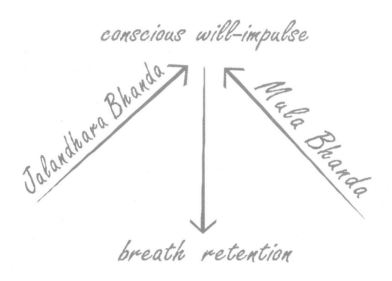

This complete breathing is difficult and should be learnt gradually. The respiratory muscles open wide so that space is created for the unfolding of the lungs. Avoid any pressure on the inhalation. The breathing should always flow evenly and gently. Every hidden corner of the lungs is filled through the gentle breathing.

Release both bhandas and breathe out again to the right. When the lungs are empty, inhale in a flowing breath; finally pull the rib-cage up even higher to Jalandhara Bhanda and hold Mula Bhanda through focussed contraction of the lower muscles. The breath retention is followed by an exhalation on the left and an inhalation, also on the left. Then after retention, breathe out again to the right and in to the right, etc.

This breathing is an art. First begin with a few rounds. One must practise the technique carefully over a few weeks until one gains confidence in practice.

Initially it will be difficult for you to keep the body relaxed despite the bhandas. Do not over-exert yourself. Once you have understood the technique, begin with a rhythm of ten seconds breathing in and ten to fifteen seconds breathing out. The holding time can be increased, beginning with ten seconds up to twenty seconds.

A rhythm of ten seconds breathing in, twenty seconds holding and fifteen seconds breathing out is good. However allow yourself a few weeks, as the long breathing rhythm should be developed from within through concentration. Do not try to impose this rhythm on the body. If calm and inwardness are found, then one requires little oxygen and as a result can retain the breath for a long time. The thinking becomes slower and concentration develops from the innermost regions.

If the period of breath retention becomes too much of a strain during the exercise, then you have over-exerted yourself. Then simply continue to breathe in an even rhythm without breath retention and bhandas. The more you listen to the breathing and bring about a rhythmical flowing, the more detached your thinking becomes and the more easily the breath can then also be held.

Let go of everything external whilst practising. Observe the flowing in and out of the air at the nose. Direct your gaze inwards while you hold the breath with the bhandas tightly locked. The skin of the body remains relaxed. It is a wide field that you are working. Thus the body is the tiny section which is being worked on. That which grows and reaches maturity is the inner. It is not the body; it is beyond it.

Do not try to achieve something with Pranayama. Practise with love for life. Do not take yourself to be important as a person. The breath overcomes your outer form. In your inner, thinking, feeling and wanting are raised to a new dimension. Dedicate the exercise to the greater, to existence, to life. At the beginning this exercise can be practised for a few minutes. With time, increase up to ten to fifteen minutes. The maximum duration should not exceed thirty minutes.

Pranayama with bhandas brings a strong effect of heat. It is possible that you will start to sweat during practice. Hold the breath resolutely but not wilfully.

Remain with your consciousness in the inner, but do not hold on to the thinking with the bhandas.

If fear arises during the breath retention, stop the exercise. From time to time it makes sense to consult a teacher who is familiar with the exercises and the effects they produce. Special caution is advised above all when uneasiness or fear arises.

Complete breathing only applies to Pranayama exercises with bhandas. Under no circumstances try to breathe in this way during other exercises, as this complete inhalation does not correspond to the natural movement of breath. If you were to try to breathe in this way other than during this exercise, the nervous system would come into heightened tension and the whole of life would be brought into imbalance. The exercise is a conscious and purposeful interference with the rhythm and with the quality of the breathing. With it a spiritual force for life is gathered. During the day, the breathing must consciously be left in peace.

Pranayama is a very rapid path towards self-realisation. It requires very great resolve, discipline and above all, conscious working into life. In strictly schooling the breathing; in drastically changing its rhythm and natural movement, the student detaches himself completely from his past. Through the effects of carbon dioxide, he builds himself a new body. The soul powers are brought into a new relationship to each other. Thus the entire life of the individual is changed. A path is taken into the pathless. There is nothing on earthly ground that could give support to the Pranayama student. One must always remain conscious of this danger.

The every-day is transient. Sorrow and joy, pain and pleasure, worry and confidence are expressions of life. The inner creates the outer. He who practises Pranayama enters into the consciousness of the inner. He does not experience the world, but experiences life in its actual depth.

If one were ready with the whole of one's heart to live the love of the inner, one would not need to make use of any exercise or technique for forming the consciousness. One would be one with oneself and with all beings. But one is dissatisfied with the events of the day and therefore wishes to have a different consciousness. This is a disastrous thought, as it leads to spiritual egoism. One's own desire to possess is carried into the spiritual region.

Thus one must examine one's motivation with particular care. He who practises Pranayama with the thought of wanting to possess, will lose everything; on the other hand he who practises with selflessness and devotion will receive a great reward.

The path of spiritual development

In our time many paths to self-discovery and self-realisation are suggested. An extensive supply of literature is at man's disposal today. For example, there is the path of Yoga of the East. In Western culture, this has met with wide acclaim. For most people this path is easily accessible and furthermore it is free from religious opinions and claims. In contrast, the paths in the West lean very strongly towards Christianity. The Christian-Gnostic schooling is the most essential of these. It is very difficult to access as it is based on a meditative comprehension of the Bible. Many branches have developed from these principal directions.

Spiritual schooling is very problematic. One cannot grasp the spirit by material means. Man always wants to obtain a recipe for self-realisation, but there is no recipe for this, nor will there ever be. If a book describes one, it is based on a big misunderstanding. One cannot enter into the absolute through a specific kind of meditation or through an exercise. The path of practice is a very active confrontation with one's personal life and with the life of others. One works concretely into the connections of the every-day and thus acquires understanding in a higher sense. This understanding ultimately gives insight and leads to expansion of the consciousness. Meditations, breathing- and physical-exercises serve to support the path through life, so that with their help an inner thought permeates one's way of acting in every-day life.

The general summary of a schooling suggested here should not be understood as a scheme. It should only give an overview and contribute to a deepening of the breath work in a broader sense. It does not lean towards an Eastern or Western schooling.

The first point on this path is *attention*. The student observes life, steers his thoughts towards the different events of daily life and thus becomes conscious of many interconnections and subtleties. Everything he does and everything that approaches him is observed more attentively and is thus more consciously processed. Nutrition is also a field that is dealt with more consciously. One gains various insights and thus becomes acquainted with many necessities as well as new duties. The student does not have to become conscious of life's deepest interconnections straight away; he must only learn to observe and must then be more able to feel into things. Just as he first notices a dew drop on a twig in the morning light and thus feels a lively stirring in his mind, he will also experience more sensitivity in his inner in observing his fellow men, and through this he will show more understanding towards individually different personalities.

The second point is *becoming aware*. That which was learnt through attention must now be expanded through an inner view. The individual must become conscious of the great power which is of spiritual origin. He steers his attention towards the various fields of life, grasps life-situations more thoroughly and from this process of sensing and observing life he becomes conscious of the great working-power which prevails throughout the world. Deep down he has a notion of the spiritual power which permeates all matter, all phenomena and events of life. There is nothing in life that lies outside this power. Everything is subject to it. It cannot be seen with the physical eyes, yet it is real and determines the outer happening. Becoming aware means that the individual recognises the divine power in his life and in the life of others. It means that he no longer dismisses the events of everyday life as mere incidents, but attributes a significance to them. He learns to observe the outer situation from a deeper stand-point and thus gains a notion of spiritual reality. He becomes more conscious of the actual, carrying forces of life.

The third stage of this general schooling does not take place separately from the two preceding steps. Nevertheless this stage forms the key to actual life. So far it has been only a knowledge within existence; an intensified process of becoming conscious in life. Now follows *inner participation* in that which was given by the preparatory schooling of the consciousness. The student must search within his heart, and there, not outside in outer happenings, he must stay. Now he directly senses the centre of his heart, thus opening his being. Eyes which are at the heart become noticeable sense organs. With these eyes, he grasps the outer situation and recognises an inner life impulse in himself and in others. He noticeably feels a connectedness with infinity, and with this eye which is seated deep within his inner, he sees his fellow men and his environment. Just as the senses perceive the world, so he must view life with the eye of the heart. With this he creates for himself the bridge between outer recognition and inner participation. Directly within himself he finds the key of life. This opens to him the gate to the great expansiveness of spiritual life on worldly ground. He participates in all events and combines outer recognition with inner power and with a fine breath of love. He no longer remains only an observer, but combines his practical life with infinite life. He feels himself as a link in the great chain of existence. There is nothing within him which might not be connected with the whole. For him there is no separation in life; he is one with himself and thus one with all.

The student must work towards this stage of development for a long time. Life is only very slowly enriched with spiritual tones, but every serious aspirant will sense and experience this stage. The separation in the personality is overcome with the eyes of the heart and a consciousness of unity arises. The preparatory stages of observing and becoming aware will never be completely over, as activity of the soul is always necessary. A dynamic gliding back and forth will sometime distance one further from the experience of the heart; sometimes guide one closer again. However, that which arises more and more on this level of learning and inner growing, is of a magnificent nature. With increasing development of the eyes at the heart, a sense for the aesthetic will take shape. It is not just perception of some kind of beauty, but it is true aesthetic. This can only awaken in the heart. The aspirant will develop artistic sensing on this path of realisation. He comprehends the world from an inner, productive side and grows into the world with the power of his heart. He finds with his heart the identification with his destiny, and through this he senses the great, working love in his personal evolution. He experiences himself, he experiences his fellow men and his entire environment as if carried on hands by this loving power.

Everyone who strives for self-realisation must pass through these stages. Thus life in the outer becomes stable and strong. However, it does not become bound to the world, but becomes permeated with a deep power of understanding and thus redeemed from all heaviness of attachment.

To be able to lastingly experience the powers of the heart, it is helpful to observe the following points. To actively carry them out requires a goal-orientated will, as well as a disciplined, conscious attitude to life.

Stability at the level of the heart is not easy, as every thought and every deed has an effect on the heart. If any disharmony exists in one's being, then the heart closes up. The first point which must be observed is tolerance. This is a big word, and whoever is honest knows how difficult the adherence to this virtue is. Tolerance allows the inner side of the heart to blossom. This side of loving understanding is promoted through reflection on situations and attentive observation of life's circumstances. It is not superficial thinking that is meant here. Through deep pondering, every situation can be explained. The thinking must indeed really be ready to appreciate the other; it must not be loaded with prejudice. If one lives true tolerance, one opens one's inner and gives the warmth of one's heart to one's fellow men. This is of decisive significance. If this tolerance becomes an inner experience, the whole world can be seen. It carries the power of the individual out into the world and opens up life from within.

Furthermore, one must develop in oneself order in thinking and acting. Here one must observe that these powers of the soul are not rigidly controlled from the head, but that things are ordered from within, that is again from the warmth of the heart. The thoughts should not wander around in a confused and aimless way, but should accompany life distinctly and with a clear intention. One's action should also be in harmony with one's thinking. Through inwardness the wandering thought can be calmed and thus the intended action can also be performed single-mindedly. One's own will becomes composed and the mind becomes harmonised.

These powers of the soul, thinking and wilful acting, are active qualities of the personality and they must be constantly promoted through conscious activities in life. Every individual must deal with his environment. Above all he must question the conditions in his relationships. Work is likewise an important aspect which should be seriously examined. Through dealing with it actively, one can give deeper meaning and content to the relationships which one leads and to the work which one carries out daily. One orders one's life through deep thinking and well-considered acting.

Caution is called for, however, in order not to violate the true duties of life through one's spiritual wanting. The one thing must not grow beyond the other, as otherwise the personality does not develop in the right ratio and the heart, as the centre of life, closes up. One's own motivation to desire things and to work towards a particular position of pre-eminence is a great danger. Daily life with its phenomena is the servant of inner growth. It shows duties and demands for every aspirant. The goal does not exist in dominating life from above, but in recognition from within and in thus bringing about that order in the personality.

The physical exercises of Yoga and the exercises of the Free Breath School contribute to order and stability in the personality. They train the will without making it hard outwardly, and they expand one's potential by setting free unused energies. Through listening to the breathing, the thinking is internalised and thus opened for further insights. All Yoga, breath and spiritual exercises should be considered a carrier-medium. They should open the personality for a wide consciousness and help to integrate one's individual abilities in a holistic sense.

Through this ordering of life and through conscious dealing with the various events of existence, a very special question emerges for everyone. The individual does not walk the path of spiritual practice for just any random reason. He is a seeker who perceives the need for consciously dealing with life and with its hidden laws. The individual does not know where the path leads him. The question of purpose and action will be revealed. Deep down, he has a notion of magnificent powers; but for a long time these remain only a very dim perception. However they have a decisive implication; an enormous driving force is connected with them.

It is necessary that one takes time at least once a day and directs one's gaze into one's inner. This can be introduced with an exercise of the free breath school. Then the consciousness is freer from outer impressions and thus much more ready to accept deeper messages.

One practises contemplation on spiritual life in the form of a silent meditation or prayer. In doing so one must not deviate from strict regularity. One always sits down at a certain time in a pleasant place and turns one's gaze inwards. The outer haste and demands of daily life must be completely released during this time. The subtle body will then adjust to this rhythm and a need for this contemplation will eventually automatically arise.

By regularly withdrawing his attention from outer events and impressions, the student recognises that it is he who determines the events. It is his thoughts which are born out of his own source and appear outwardly. This view inwards is a significant process of becoming conscious. One realises more and more that there is nothing in outer life which can bring lasting fulfilment. One's own stand-point becomes more conscious, and outer life can be shaped from within. That force which is the only power in life; that inner impulse which creates everything outer in its forms, will reveal itself in the present.

The last point of this general portrayal is of decisive significance. One could call it the power of fate. Everybody, whether he lives in simple or affluent circumstances has the desire for activities in life. Many different desires are kindled in the individual stages of life. Nobody seriously wants to live in solitude, without participating in worldly events. Seclusion and separation from present culture could also never lead to the goal, to self-realisation. Thus our life is determined by an enormous split. This split is bound to arise through one's own wishes and through the simultaneously existing claim for spiritual realisation. Through our very selves we determine the power of fate. On the one hand we want to have something for ourselves; on the other hand we want freedom of the soul. But as soon as we want something, absolute freedom cannot be attained. Thus the power of fate lives in us.

Everyone must be born from above. Man's own desire cannot lead him to the spirit, but he can only prepare himself so that something greater works through him. Freedom of the soul requires selflessness. As long as man wants to have freedom, he cannot become free. He must be redeemed from above.

The path of Yoga in the classical sense describes absolute dispassion and suggests fasting and hard ascetic practices. Other, older paths of schooling also describe this and demand denial and renunciation. However these would be paths of separation and denial of life. They cannot be walked any more. The values for inner schooling have changed decisively in the course of the centuries. We must accept our fate and participate actively in life. The path would become hopeless if we withdrew from outer existence into solitude.

It is the desires in life which have a determining effect on fate. Every individual has gathered experiences in a certain way. These experiences in turn determine his wanting for the future. Some people long for a small paradise, some for peace on earth, some want to improve society and others again want to realise the idealism of a world philosophy. Thus the power of fate leads inescapably to new insights and deeper experiences. The feeling of separation works in us continuously.

142

The forces which spring from desires are important driving forces for life. If there were no desires then there would not be any further development either. With the outer desire there simultaneously works an inner desire in the soul. It is that ideal thought of existence; it springs from one's innermost wanting and leads us irrefutably to a point of friction. Through attentive schooling and gaining a sense of the inner aspects of life the consciousness is prepared and one will learn to appreciate life in its own greatness. This greatness is the only and lasting reality.

There is only the one power. It is active over the entire earth; it has no beginning and no end. That must be acknowledged in the soul. All deeds and actions, all desires are dedicated to this greater reality. With this the power of fate disappears.

The name which was given to an individual describes the outer. This outer must be placed at the feet of the greater reality. Thus one's own name is fused with the universal name. Recognition is followed by understanding and understanding is followed by devotion.

One's desires are not repressed; one's desires are dedicated to the greater reality. Thus the seeker reaps not the reward of his work, but he reaps the reward of life. This is love.

This devotion can only occur at a very mature stage of consciousness. It cannot occur without the active school of life and without active realisation in the personal. It leads to selflessness and thus to freedom of the soul. The scope of the spiritual is greater than the capacity of the individual. With devotion to life a breath of reality is experienced and the carrying power of love reveals itself.

Other titles by Heinz Grill
available in English:

The Soul Dimension of Yoga

A practical foundation for a new way of Yoga

Yoga and Christianity

A foundation for a Christian-spiritual
way of meditation and practice